Anesthesiology
Boards Made Easy

Anesthesiology Boards Made Easy

A physician's step-by-step guide to make
your board preparation successful

JEFF STEINER, DO, MBA

Copyright © 2017 Jeff Steiner, DO, MBA
Published by Two Pugs Publishing, LLC

Two Pugs Publishing, LLC
401 North Carroll Avenue—Suite #206
Southlake, TX 6092

ISBN: 0989840158
eISBN: 9780989840156

Disclaimer

MATERIAL IN THIS book is for educational purposes only and does not constitute medical or career advice or create a doctor-patient relationship. The book and the pages referenced in this book on the related website, AnesthesiaMadeEasy.com, are intended for physicians who are working toward their board certification in anesthesiology through the American Board of Anesthesiology (ABA).

The reader cannot rely on a single book for board certification preparation. This book is intended as an overview and guide, and is by no means exhaustive in its scope. The American Board of Anesthesiology (ABA), the American Society of Anesthesiology (ASA), and the American Council on Graduate Medical Education (ACGME) are constantly changing their rules and regulations related to anesthesiology resident training and board certification in anesthesiology. It is the responsibility of the reader to determine the current rules and regulations related to anesthesiology resident training and board certification in anesthesiology.

DISCLAIMER

Care has been taken to confirm that the information presented is correct and is in line with generally accepted practices. That being said, the author, editors, contributors, peer reviewers and publisher are not responsible for errors or omissions of information or for any direct or indirect consequences of the application of information in this book and website AnesthesiaMadeEasy.com. Neither the author, editors, contributors, peer reviewers, nor the publisher make any warranty, express or implied, or assume any liability for injury and/or damage to persons or property arising out of or related to any use of the material contained in this book. Ultimately, success or otherwise at the board certification rests on the physician.

I am not an ABA Examiner, and I don't write questions for any of the ABA exam. (I wouldn't be able to write this book if I did those activities.) I have taken the ABA boards for both Anesthesiology and Pediatric Anesthesiology and passed them both the first time. I helped others successfully prepare for the boards and through this book, I can help you as well.

This book is not endorsed by the ASA, ABA, ACGME, or any affiliated groups.

No residents, program directors, or oral board examiners were harmed in the making of this book!

Why You Need *Anesthesiology Boards Made Easy*

WHEN YOU BECAME an anesthesiology resident, no one told you that you would have a full-time job as an anesthesiology resident learning your craft **and** be a full-time student getting ready for more exams. It's great you are getting a paycheck for your work, but you still need to study for yet another set of board exams. Trying to balance these two roles is difficult when there is so much to learn and in a relatively short amount of time. Since these exams will cost you both time and money, you want to only take them once.

With such a high-stakes game, where do you begin? This insider's strategy guide will show you how to successfully pass your exams and become board certified. You have spent hundreds of thousands of dollars to get a college degree, a medical degree, and for the extensive training you have taken so far to get you where you are now.

Why not do everything you can to ensure your continuing success? You want a viable career as an anesthesiologist.

After all, if you were going to play a challenging game, you would try to figure out the objectives, rules, knowledge, strategy, tactics, and skills (plus a little luck) to win, right?

In this book, I will give you a road map to explain how the boards work, how to make your studying more efficient and less painful, and how to prepare for the most challenging exam of your career: the dreaded Applied Exam. (It is a seventy-minute, oral exam void of multiple-choice questions given to you by experts in the field of anesthesiology. Some of the oral board examiners wrote the very books you will study to take the exam.)

With the integrated approach presented in this book, *Anesthesiology Boards Made Easy* will not only help you learn the material for the Boards but also help you become a better anesthesiologist as well.

This is not a book that will tell you how to cheat the system. On the contrary, I will teach you the rules, so that you can make the system work for you. I will help you build your own strategy and tactics, because while there are some guidelines, there is no recipe that will work for everyone every time.

Even with the many hacks I give you throughout this book, it is still going to take hard work, hours of study, and hours of preparation to make success possible. This book should help you find the process more manageable.

As a former chief resident of a large anesthesiology residency program, double Boarded pediatric anesthesiologist, and a father of two boys, I know what it is like to try and balance studying, residency, and a family life. Now, as a fellowship program director, I see residents and fellows making some of the same mistakes I had made. I have also seen what works well for the new, revised Anesthesiology Board exams.

In the chapters that follow, I'll teach you how to integrate your studying, how to prepare for the ABA Basic, Advanced, and Applied exams; starting while you are still an intern.

The techniques described in this book have been used by residents to successfully become board-certified anesthesiologists. I helped an anesthesiologist to pass the oral boards on his second time around, after he had failed it the first time! (The chances of passing the oral exam the first time is around 85 percent. Those who fail and have to retake the exam have a pass rate in the 60 percent range.) He already had the knowledge, but I taught him how to use it. The techniques I taught him are in this book so that you can have a good chance at passing it the first time.

What are you waiting for? You have worked too hard to get into anesthesiology residency training to blow it on not being able to become board certified.

Continue reading *Anesthesiology Boards Made Easy* and build strategies, tactics, and skills into your studying which will help you become board certified with the least amount of pain possible.

A Note on Anesthesiology Nomenclature

If you have been in an anesthesia residency for any period of time, then you can skip this section. If, however, you are new to anesthesiology training, or you are transferring from another specialty, this chapter is for you.

In most residency-training programs, residents are classified by their number of years out of medical school. First-year residents (commonly called interns) are classified as postgraduate year—One (PGY-1) residents. Second-year residents are PGY-2 and so forth.

In anesthesiology training, the PGY-1 year is classified as the clinical base year (CBY). The second year of training is classified as clinical anesthesia—One (CA-1) year and so forth.

PGY-1 = R1 = CBY = intern year
PGY-2 = R2 = CA-1
PGY-3 = R3 = CA-2
PGY-4 = R4 = CA-3
PGY-5 = R5 = CA-4 = Fellow

There are two different types of anesthesiology residency-training programs offered in the National Resident Matching Program (NRMP) Match: categorical and advanced.

Categorical Programs include the CB year within the training structure and include the CA-1, CA-2, and CA-3 years for a total of four years in length.

Advanced Programs only include the last three years of training (CA-1, CA-2, and CA-3). For these programs, you have to either do your intern year at another program or you are a transfer from another specialty where you have already completed your intern year. All anesthesiology residents must complete three total years of anesthesiology training, in addition to an intern year, to be eligible to become board certified in anesthesiology.

Anesthesiology Boards Resources

Preparing for the Board Certification process is a dynamic event. Probably the day this book goes to print, there will be new information about the process. New books are written, new articles posted to the web, and more resources are put on the Internet.

I don't want you to miss out on the opportunity to access these new materials.

Throughout this book, you will see web links that will take you to a page that has an article with more information, a collection of links to other resources, or books that will help you become board certified in anesthesiology.

I have organized all the webpages related to this book in one place at **AnesthesiaMadeEasy.com/ababoards**.

You can always stop by there when you have some time and see what we have to offer.

While you are online, please take a moment to stop by **Amazon.com** and review our book. ~ Thanks

~Jeff Steiner, DO, MBA

Dr. Steiner's Other Books

Anesthesia Made Easy: The Survival Guide to Make Your First Anesthesia Rotation a Success anesthesiamadeeasy.com/book

Physician's Guide to Personal Finance: The Review Guide for the Class You Should Have Had in Medical School anesthesiamadeeasy.com/personal-finance

Acknowledgments

Peer Reviewers

I WANT TO thank the following peer reviewers who went through the material in this book to make a product of which I am truly proud.

You all really made the book much better than I could have hoped for.

If there are errors or omissions, they rest squarely on the shoulders of the author and publisher of this book.

Ravi Bhoja, MD
Kristina Goff, MD
Tally Goldfarb, MD
Russell K. McAllister, MD
Megan Maxwell, MD
Jaffer Odeh, MD
Amy Woods, MD

Cover Design: Daryl C. Orosco at DARYL-CONCIPTO™ through 99desings.com
Content Layout: CreateSpace Interior Design
Content Editing: Roma at CreateSpace Editing

Contents

Section One

The Game

This is your game, Nicholas, and welcome to it. I'm here to let you in on a few ground rules...The object of The Game is to discover the object of...The Game.

—*THE GAME* WITH MICHAEL DOUGLAS

1

Playing the Game of Becoming a Board Certified Anesthesiologist

Why become board certified?

WHILE I AM not aware of any large-scale studies showing that board certification reduces bad patient outcomes, it is the closest thing we have to trying to show competency.

Because our "game" is one with very high stakes, a lot of time and energy goes into becoming board certified. You might have heard about a faculty at your institution who is not boarded, or the private practice anesthesiologist who has been practicing for years without board certification...but these types of stories are becoming outliers.

Most anesthesiologists today will have to be boarded to have a successful, and long, career in medicine. Even if you are planning on joining a group without being boarded, your job may depend on it in the future. Board certification may also determine the size of your paycheck and maybe a requirement for advancement within your group. For example, the hospital where I work (and many others) has a policy that in order to be on staff, you have to become boarded in your specialty within six years of starting work. In private practice, your ability to become a full partner might be hampered. Also, you have to be boarded (or board eligible) to get credentialed at every hospital at which you work.

Rules for completing your board certification

In order to become board certified by the American Board of Anesthesiology (ABA), you will go through the following process:

1. Graduate from medical school
2. Get accepted into an ACGME-accredited anesthesiology residency program
3. Pass all three Steps the USMLE/COMLEX
4. Pass the ABA Basic exam
5. Graduate from an ACGME-accredited anesthesiology residency program
6. Pass the ABA Advanced exam
7. Pass the ABA Applied exam
8. Have an unrestricted medical license
9. Do not have any drug or alcohol problems

These are "hard stop" rules. There is no bending or getting around them.

Take full advantage of your residency training

Residents usually think of the board certification exams like the USMLE or COMLEX. You take just one exam at a time and move on to the next one after the previous one is passed. The ABA board exams are more integrated. Studying for your Basic exam will help you with your Advanced exam and Applied exam. There is more overlap in the types of questions you will be asked than what you saw on the USMLE or COMLEX.

If you start thinking about the process early, you will make the most of your time and training. You will be given opportunities during residency that are not as readily available after you graduate. Many of the practice exams that you take during residency are paid for by your department; you have ready access to oral exam preparation and lectures on board topics, and you are in an environment that promotes learning and education. Once you graduate, it becomes more difficult to maintain this type of environment on your own, especially when your job is not about training, but about getting cases done.

You need to learn a new game

When you were a premed student, you played a game called "Get into Medical School."

You knew the rules: get good grades, do well on the MCAT, do some volunteer work, get some letters from doctors describing how great a doctor you will be, write a compelling personal statement, and interview well.

When you were a medical student, you played a very similar game called "Get into Anesthesiology residency."

You used very similar rules: get good grades, do well on the Step 1 & 2 exams, do some volunteer work, do well on your anesthesiology rotation, get some letters from anesthesiologists saying what a great anesthesiologist you will be one day, write a personal statement, and interview well.

Like most residents that get into anesthesiology residency, you probably feel like the game is over.

You have won.

You just have to "survive training" and get to the good stuff...working as a "real doctor" and making some "real money."

One game is done, but another one has begun: the game of board certification.

This "new game" has a new set of objectives, rules, strategy, tactics and skills that you have not had to use before. What is worse, you may not even know you are playing a new game.

This isn't about getting into another training program, it's about showing the ABA that you are competent enough to call yourself a Diplomate of the board and becoming a member of a very select group of physicians.

In this "new game," there is no class rank, no volunteer work, no rotation grades, and no personal statements. Instead, it consists of three exams, the American Board of Anesthesiology (ABA) Basic, Advanced, and Applied exams.

This new game has some new objectives, rules, strategy, tactics, skills, and knowledge to learn. When you put these components to work, you are well on your way to board certification.

The seven components to playing your new game

You know, Hobbes, some days even my lucky rocket ship underpants don't help.

—CALVIN

In this new game of board certification, you will need to learn a new system. Trying to use the old systems to play this new game is possible, but you using the old system to get through the process will require brute force, and it will be painful. I will teach you how to do it with finesse.

It is a pity that most residents only use a few of the components to try and win the game.

You on the other hand, will be playing a new game and using a new system to pass the "boards." You will be using all seven components of game play to crush it. It's about working smarter, not harder.

This new game has seven components, used at different times, which you can use to successfully become board certified in anesthesiology.

1. Objectives

- The main objective is to become a board certified anesthesiologist. In order to reach this milestone, you have to graduate from anesthesiology residency and pass the three-part exam for the ABA.

2. Rules

- Many residents don't take the time to learn the rules of the game. When you understand the rules of the game, you are not completely reliant on someone else for your education. Knowing the set of rules and understanding how to use them, will help you take better control of your training, education, and ultimately board certification.
- Knowing the rules will also help you complete the objectives of the game.

3. Anesthesia knowledge

- This component is the one that most residents lean on the most.
- Anesthesia knowledge is the most intuitive component and one that you can have the most control over. It also happens to be the component that is the least sophisticated endeavor because, if you study enough, you will learn the "book smarts" of anesthesiology.

- Through brute force you can use anesthesia knowledge for the board exams and hope to pass. Or, you can also use the other components and win the board certification game easier.

4. Strategy

- Strategy is the big picture of what you want to accomplish.
- This is where you come up with a plan for each objective. You will set goals for each one of the objectives you need to complete.
- **For example:** You decide that you want to reach a specific scaled score, like thirty for example, on the In-Training Exam (ITE) next year. That is a measurable goal, and it also provides more structure than "I want to do well."

5. Tactics

- Tactics are the plans, tasks, and procedure of how you will accomplish your strategy.
- It is your plan of how you will actually carry out the strategy.
- **In the example above**, because you want to obtain a scaled score of thirty on the ITE next year, you set up a study schedule with milestones to hit each week. This will keep you on task and at a reasonable study pace. You decide you will read through the chapter

of OB anesthesia during your OB month and complete fifty questions during the month as well. Recall that percentiles vary widely each year and a significant growth in knowledge will be required to simply "maintain" a specific percentile.

6. Skills

- This final controllable component is perhaps the least developed by most anesthesiology residents. But you won't be like most residents, right?
- There will be clinical skills that you will master in your residency (intubation, central line placement, epidurals, etc.), and then there are the skills that you need to develop to pass the exams. These didactic skills are the ones we will concentrate on in *Anesthesiology Boards Made Easy*.
- You will need to develop skills to do well on the Basic and Advanced exams and certainly on the Applied exam. I will help coach you on how to develop these skills throughout your residency, so that your studying will be more effective and you will arrive at each exam well prepared.

7. Luck/providence/good or bad fortune

- This is perhaps the second most used component by most residents but the one you have the least influence over. You hope that you are not asked too many questions on stuff you don't know. You try to study "high-yield" material and figure that the less common stuff won't be asked.

- There is also some gambling that you will know just enough to pass the exam, because it is a pass/fail report that you receive.
- Don't let your board certification be left up to luck. The better you know the objectives, rules, anesthesia knowledge, strategy, tactics, and develop your exam skills, the less luck you need.
- The more you understand the game, and learn the knowledge, the less reliant you will be on this component of the game.

2

The Objective of the Game

MOST ANESTHESIOLOGY RESIDENTS want to become well-trained anesthesiologists. That is a nebulous objective. How do you prove or measure when you become a "well-trained anesthesiologist?"

For most anesthesiologists, the way you show that you are well trained, is to be board certified. This is also the metric by which others will judge you before they know you. This includes anesthesia groups as well as hospitals and hospital committees.

Can there be a board-certified anesthesiologist who is not well trained? Sure. But board certification is a system that has been developed to try and validate your training and experience.

That is the point of this game.

The object of the game of being board certified is simple: become board certified.

That seems pretty simple, and it is simple.

In order to reach the main objective, there are three sub-objectives you must concentrate on:

1. Doing well on your written board exams (ABA Basic and Advanced)
2. Graduating from anesthesiology residency
3. Passing your ABA Applied exam

You probably already intuitively know that you need to concentrate on these areas. Thankfully, there is a lot of overlap between these objectives. Doing well on your exams will help you graduate from residency and help you become board certified. Graduation from residency is a requirement for board certification. As you prepare for board certification, you will do well on your exams, and you will graduate from residency.

Let's take each one of these, and I will walk you through how to accomplish each one.

In Section #2, we will concentrate on the first, large objective: Doing well on your written board exams.

Section Two

Doing Well on Your Written Exams

MOST RESIDENTS ONLY talk about the hard, clinical work of residency. You have heard (and probably told others) about nights on call, the procedures, the "mean" attendings, the last gruesome trauma, and the cases that went sideways in a hurry.

What you have probably been neglected to be told about is the challenge of continuing to study for various exams while you are a resident.

There are multiple exams you will be taking during your training as an anesthesiology resident. Most will be done on a computer and one will be an oral exam. Building your base of anesthesia knowledge will help you with all of these exams.

- **USMLE/COMLEX Step 3**
  - Hopefully taken only once at some point during your intern year

- **In-Training Exam (ITE)**
    - Taken every year during your residency, typically in the month of February
- **Anesthesia Knowledge Exam (AKT)**
    - Some programs use these, others do not.
    - Can be taken at one month, six months, and twenty-four months of training and called the AKT-1, AKT-6, and AKT-24.
- **Basic Exam**
    - Taken at the end of the CA-1 year
    - This is a "hard stop" exam—you eventually have to pass it to graduate from residency
- **Advanced Exam**
    - Taken in the July after graduation from residency
- **Applied Exam**
    - Known as the "oral exam" until the recent board exam change
    - The Applied exam consists of Standardized Oral Examination (SOE) and the Objective Structured Clinical Exam (OSCE).
    - Cannot be taken until successful completion of the Advanced exam

Some residents rely on their anesthesiology residency training to provide the knowledge and skills needed to pass the exams. They think that they can get their didactic training by just showing up at lectures, doing a little studying on their own, and then cram for the exam.

Doing well on the ITE is **not enough** to get you through the written exam. Do not rely on your scores on the ITE to get you through the Basic and Advanced exams. Each exam is a challenge in itself.

The sub-objective of doing well on your exams is critical to winning the game.

3

Anesthesia Knowledge: Mastering the Exams

KNOWING HOW TO study for each exam is important. Knowing what to focus on, what to expect, and how to prepare is key to doing well on these exams.

USMLE/COMLEX Step 3

"Two months, two weeks, two pencils"...kind of.

I am sure by now you have heard the phrase of "two months, two weeks, two pencils" to describe the USMLE/COMLEX boards. Two months to study for Step 1, two weeks to study for Step 2, and two pencils (basically just show up) to take Step 3.

Don't believe it.

I know several physicians who took this philosophy to heart and **failed Step 3**. As embarrassing as this is, what is worse is that once you fail:

1. You have to study for and retake Step 3, and
2. You will continue to postpone your anesthesiology board study, because you have to be studying for Step 3.

When should you take Step 3?

Have a plan to study for the Step 3 exam well in advance of taking it. You will want to get this exam knocked out so that you have time to start studying for the ITE. The longer you wait, the harder it will be to pass Step 3 because your training will be specializing in anesthesiology during your CA-1 through CA-3 years.

Each state is a little different as to when you can sit for the USMLE/COMLEX. Some allow you to sit for the exam as soon as you start residency, and others make you wait until you finish your PGY-1/CB year. If you are given the choice, I recommend sitting for the exam about six months into your training. It helps to have some practical experience before taking the exam, and it gives you a chance to become acclimated to your intern year.

Some states also have a limited number of chances to sit for the exam. For example, in Texas, you have three opportunities to take the exam; after that, you will **never be able to obtain a Texas medical license**.

Never.

Use the techniques in chapter 5 (**How to Study as a Resident**) and take the studying for Step 3 seriously.

If you are a DO, sitting for the COMLEX Step 3, don't forget to brush up on your osteopathic manipulative medicine questions.

I have review books and other resources listed for you to help you prepare at AnesthesiaMadeEasy.com/step3.

In-Training Exam (ITE)

Most specialties have exams that their residents take during their training, and anesthesiology residents are no exception. You will be taking the In-Training Exam (ITE) each year throughout your anesthesiology program. This is a computerized exam that is a metric that you can use to compare yourself to other residents across the country.

The ITE is prepared by the ABA and given to every anesthesiology resident, each year in February. It contains content from both the ABA Basic and Advanced exams. It is a great opportunity to prepare for the ABA exams, because the ITE is the equivalent of a full-length exam given in the same testing environment.

Most fellowships will look at your ITE scores (and your Basic exam) to see how likely you will become board certified. If you are struggling with ITEs, and might not pass the Advanced and Applied exams, then fellowships might be hesitant to take you on as a fellow. This is important because your CA-1 ITE will be what fellowship directors have to judge you on. The applications may be due before your CA-2 ITE scores are known, depending on the subspecialty.

You will get some great information on the ITE in chapter 5 and also at AnesthesiaMadeEasy.com/ite to help you with your ITE.

The Anesthesia Knowledge Exam (AKT)

The Anesthesia Knowledge Exam (AKT) is a set of exams prepared by an independent company that is not part of the ACGME, the Resident Review Committee (RRC), ABA, or ASA. Because of this, these exams are not mandated by these groups for graduation or board certification. (However, your department might have a policy related to the score you receive, so please check with them.)

The company that produces these exams has validated them, so they still hold merit.

Some anesthesiology residency-training programs use these exams to see how you compare with other residents around the country.

The AKT exams are named based on when they are given to you, as stated in the section 2 introduction.

These are great opportunities to take a practice exam and see how you stack up against other residents around the country.

Don't blow these off. You should welcome any opportunity to take an anesthesiology standardized exam.

The ABA Board Exams

The ABA Board Exams are the real thing. You will have been studying and working as a "clinical anesthesiology resident" for a full year before you take the first "real" exam that counts toward broad certification. You will be using your ITE exam scores along the way to help you prepare, but how you do on these exams will determine how you progress toward board certification.

It is important to sign up early for exams at the testing centers, since they have limited testing computers. Otherwise, you may have to travel to a distant location for the exam, which will add stress to your test day.

1. **ABA Basic Exam**—taken at the end of the CA-1 year, in June

   This is a "hard stop" exam. You have three chances to pass it during your residency. If you cannot pass this exam, you cannot progress to your CA-3 year and therefore cannot graduate. The Basic exam tests your understanding of the scientific basis of anesthesiology: pharmacology, physiology, anatomy, machines, and equipment. You have four hours and forty minutes to complete 250 multiple-guess questions. Like many of your exams since graduation from medical school, it will be taken on a computer at a testing center like your other board exams. If this exam is failed twice, the ABA mandates that you receive an "unsatisfactory" for medical knowledge for the six-month period. If it is failed again, a second "unsatisfactory" is given, which mandates an extra year of training, if your program allows you to continue.

2. **ABA Advanced Exam**—taken after you graduate from residency, in July

    This exam focuses on the clinical aspects of anesthesiology including advanced techniques and subspecialty areas. You can't forget the information that you learned for the ABA Basic exam, because it will be applied at a higher level. Like the Basic exam, you have four hours and forty minutes to complete 250 multiple-choice questions. You will start to know your local testing center very well by this point.

3. **ABA Applied Exam**—taken after successfully completing the other two exams

    This is an oral board exam that tests your understanding of anesthesia knowledge at a higher level. We will go into great detail on how to prepare for this exam in chapter 17. Briefly, it consists of two stem questions, plus six smaller questions in a seventy-minute time period. The ABA is also going to add an Objective Structured Clinical Examination (OSCE), starting in March 2018. Theses exams are given at the same time at the ABA Assessment Center in Raleigh, NC.

4

General Guidelines for Doing Well on Your Exams

"**T**RAIN LIKE YOU will fight, because you will fight like you trained." This is a common saying in the military. You will fall back on your training when you are under stress. You have to practice the way you will be tested so that you will do well.

You will have multiple exams on your way to becoming board certified:

1. Figure out when you need to take the various exams, stay on schedule, and budget for hefty fees.
2. Learn what is on the exams.
    Each exam will have a content outline. Review each content outline to find out where you need to focus your studying.

3. For specific rules about each exam, download the book-let from the ABA about the staged exams. Read through it so that you know what to expect. I have some quick links for you at AnesthesiaMadeEasy.com/aba.

Many of the exams that you will take as a resident (and newly graduated anesthesiologist) will require the same preparation that you used for your MCAT and Step exams. These include the ITE, AKT, and the ABA written exams (Basic and Advanced)

Just like your other exams, you will need to get into the habit of outside reading, but more importantly, doing practice questions.

Lots of questions.

Do them on a computer, if you can, because you will be tested on a computer for your exams.

The great thing about taking the ITE every year is the ability to take a "practice exam," which will simulate the Basic and Advanced exams—in a testing center, on a computer. You will have choices and will narrow things down based on context clues.

After passing your written exam, you will take the Applied exam. For this exam, you will need to practice giving answers orally. There are no lists of answers from which to choose. During the Applied exam, you will be asked not only the answer, but the reasoning behind it. This can be challenging because, in the United States, a majority of the exams you have taken so far have been written. (You've probably never had an oral exam in your life!)

Like the written exams you take, you will need to take lots of practice oral exams when you prepare. All the studying for the Basic and Advanced exams will not go to waste, because you will use the same information for your knowledge base in the Applied exam.

Sounds hard?

It will be a challenge, but it will be easier because I will help prepare you for the exam in a way that makes the oral boards fun. (OK, not fun, but not nearly as painful.)

Using questions to study for exams

Don't simply study practice exams to learn the "right answers." To really get the most from practice questions, look at the explanations of why the answers were right or why they were wrong. This will help you with concepts, which is more valuable than memorizing a right answer. It will potentially show you gaps in your knowledge, where you need to do some more studying.

Utilizing ACE, SEA, or review question books to "memorize" the potential questions for the exam may turn out to be a losing strategy. The ABA is constantly updating the Basic and Advanced exams, so relying on old questions to get you through might not work.

You can find some resources to help you build your anesthesia knowledge at AnethesiaMadeEasy.com/abaexambooks.

5

The Strategy/Tactics/Skills of Written Exam Preparation

BRIEFLY, STRATEGY IS the "what" of the game. What are the goals you want to achieve to reach your goals? Tactics is the "how" of the game. How specifically are you going to achieve the "what?" Of course, skills are those things you are going to learn, outside of anesthesia knowledge, that will help you obtain the goal.

How to use the ITE

As stated earlier, the ITE is a great tool to use for preparation to take the ABA Basic and ABA Advanced exams. It will also help you build a base of anesthesia knowledge that you will use on the ABA Applied exam. You take it on a computer like the ABA Basic and ABA Advanced exam, which is a great opportunity to simulate the exams every year.

There are four areas where the ITE can help you:

1. **It gives you a deadline for studying.** The ITE is given every year in February. By having this date firmly put on your schedule, you are able to build a study schedule for the exam.

2. **It shows you where you are lacking.** You will be getting feedback on how your studying is progressing. When you get your results, you will be given keywords (see below) that will help with your study process. You will also be told how you did on Basic and Advanced topics.

3. **You get a measure for how you compare to other residents in your program and across the country.** Healthy competition can be a good motivator to help you study for the exam.

4. **It shows you a trajectory.** When you get your scores each year, you can track your growth of knowledge to determine whether you are likely to pass the ABA Basic and Advanced exams.

These four categories of information will provide you with an analysis of your study techniques so you can better prepare for your next exam.

Does the ITE really matter?

The ITE has no direct bearing on whether or not you become board certified. There is no requirement for graduation or to be able to sit for the Basic, Advanced, or Applied exams based on your ITE scores.

However, it might matter a lot to your program. Some programs have minimal ITE score requirements for residents who want to moonlight. It might also potentially put you on the Clinical Competency Committee (CCC) naughty list and potentially make you unsatisfactory to the ABA.

It will matter for fellowship applications. Because you will be applying to fellowships during your CA-2 year, fellowship program directors will want to see your ITE scores to see if you are on a trajectory for passing the boards. Fellowships are one-to-two year programs that train you in an anesthesia subspecialty such as pediatric anesthesia or cardiac anesthesia. Directors are looking for fellows that can pass their boards, so they can focus on their subspecialty training.

Using the content outlines and keywords to prepare for the boards

Content outline

The content outline for the exams is simply an outline of all the information that can be tested on any given exam. You can find the content outline for the ABA Basic and Advanced exams on the ABA website. (You can go to AnesthesiaMadeEasy. com/aba for links to the content outlines and other resources.)

Keywords

Keywords are "buzz words" that are related to topics on the ITE. Every year, the ABA distributes a list of keywords to your program director that is a shortened outline of all the incorrectly answered questions across the country. The keywords that are distributed to program directors change year to year, and reflect the continual evolution of the exam.

After you take your exam, you will receive a report from the ABA, along with a personal list of keywords. These two lists of keywords are a great way to focus on areas that you did not do well on the exam. These lists will give you the ability to look for trends in your own study habits, year after year.

The exam committee also sends the program directors a list of commonly misunderstood concepts for each of the written exams. Ask your program director if they will share the list with you, as it can identify areas that are challenging for the majority of the residents.

This feedback will be invaluable, especially when you are taking the ITE in your CA-1 and CA-3 years, just before you take the Basic and Advanced exams, respectively. I offer some resources for using your keywords to study for future exams at AnesthesiaMadeEasy.com/ite.

Anesthesiology knowledge: How to study as a resident

Studying for the ABA boards is a marathon. Much like the USMLE/COMPLEX, you cannot cram for this exam. Not only will you be studying for the ABA exams, you will also have the ITE, and possibly, the AKT to study for.

In medical school, you had four big advantages for studying:

1. You had one job: being a medical school student. I know some medical school students who worked during medical school, but the only job you were required to do was to be a student.
2. You had constant deadlines. You had exams every one or two weeks during the school year. These constant deadlines helped to keep you from falling behind in your studies. Even if you were a world-class procrastinator, you were still forced to study on a regular basis. If you procrastinate now, like you did in college or medical school, you will get crushed.
3. The exams you took were only over the material in your class. You had a few cumulative exams (USMLE/COMLEX Step 1 & 2) but, for the most part, they were "staged exams."
4. You had academic protections. There were probably plenty of rotations where you were cut loose from your clinical duties to go and study for your exams. During your first two years, all of the focus was on didactics and studying for exams. You probably were given months off

on regular rotations/classes to study for the USMLE/
COMLEX Step 1 & 2. Those days are gone.

During residency, you have an environment that is more difficult to study in.

1. You are now working full time at a job and still need to study. Luckily you are studying to help you in your job, and your job is helping you study for exams, so the two reinforce each other.
2. You do have deadlines, but instead of being every one or two weeks, they are now only one or two times a year.
3. All your exams are now cumulative. Not only do you have to retain the information for the year, but you have to constantly brush up on information that you learned years ago.
4. Your academic protections are less stringent than when you were a student. Because you are also part of the workforce, you have a commitment to providing medical care in addition to your studying. Much of your study time will be built into the time you have left over after you have done your job. Some of your free time will be taken up with studying for your exams and for your job.

What can you do to overcome these challenges?

There are ten techniques you can use to improve your studying as a resident.

Ten techniques for studying as a resident

Studying will take on a whole new priority because it is part of your training to become a better anesthesiologist. Here are ten techniques that will help you study when you are an anesthesiology resident, especially when you don't feel like you have enough time.

1. Build good habits.

Habit building takes time. Once you get into the habit of building studying into your free time, it will become second nature. Even making it a habit to do ten minutes of reading before you go to bed or when you wake up is a good starting point. Set a goal that you easily achieve so that it becomes successful. Then slowly add more time as you go.

Find a location that works for studying and use it. If you really like coffee, set up in a coffee shop and "bribe" yourself with being able to have some coffee while you study. You might find a location in your home. Because you will be tested with questions, it is a good idea to include some practice questions in your studying. Remember: "Train like you will fight, because you will fight like you trained."

Along with reading anesthesiology textbooks, it is a good idea to spend a fair amount of time doing practice questions. Questions are a great way to **review**, but they do not provide a **stable foundation** of knowledge to build upon. I have heard of residents who only did practice questions, missed out on some pretty important concepts, and failed the Basic exam.

2. Schedule your studying time.

A study in the *Journal of Anesthesia* in 2006 showed that residents who engaged in self-study 10.5 hours a week were well positioned to pass the ITE. By planning out your studying, you will be more likely to actually sit down and do it. When you get your call schedule, build your study time around it. When you know you are going to be stuck in-house at the hospital (especially if it is a slow rotation), plan to do a little studying, instead of vegging out for the entire time.

In the last section of this book, there is a broad overview of what to expect throughout your training in chapters 25–29.

Schedule study time with another resident so you are encouraged to study. (You will find it helpful to have a study partner for the Applied exam so that you can coach each other. You will read more about this in section four.) On the other hand, if you find studying with others is a distraction, then break it up and go at it alone sometimes.

3. Set a sustainable pace.

Your anesthesiology exams have such a large amount of information contained within them, it is impossible to cram for them. Becoming a board-certified anesthesiologist is a marathon.

You will want to build a baseline level of studying that occurs throughout the year. As you get closer to the key exams, you will want to intensify your studying so that you apply yourself for the exams and will be ready to take them.

4. Study smarter, not harder.

For every major exam that you will take as a resident, there will be a content outline provided by the USMLE / COMLEX (for Step 3) or by the ABA (for the ITE, Basic, Advanced, and Applied exams). It is easier to study those topics that you enjoy, but make sure you shore up your weaknesses. There should not be any surprises on your board exams. The ITE will also provide you with keywords after you take your exam. Use these keywords to guide your study for the next time you take it (as we discussed above).

5. Choose your anesthesiology resources thoughtfully.

Have a purpose for each resource you put into your studying arsenal. Don't buy so many resources that you get overwhelmed as to which one to use.

There are so many anesthesiology books available in print and electronic versions. Your program may have suggested resources, but rarely are there "required" books for residency. When I make suggestions on my website at AnesthesiaMadeEasy.com/abaexambooks, I try and provide a rationale for how you will use the resource. There are a lot of great books, and I try and give you a couple of different options, unless there is clearly a best alternative. You want to buy books that you will use, not sit on your shelf or take up space on your e-reader.

6. Use the Pomodoro Technique®

This technique relies on the concept that you retain more of what you learn at the start and end times of your studying. So, if you have more starts and finishes (which is really breaking your study times into shorter periods with more breaks), you should be retaining more information.

What this technique looks like is studying for twenty-five minutes, then taking a five-minute break. You get up, walk around, stretch, get a drink, then study again for a concentrated twenty-five minutes. At the end of three rounds, take some extra break time to give yourself a longer rest period.

Instead of studying for an hour straight, (with only one start and one end time), you study with a break in the middle and end up with two starts and two ends. While this doesn't sound like a big deal, it can really do wonders for your retention and your sanity.

It does two things:

1) It keeps you from multitasking so that you stay focused on the material at hand. It will keep you on task.
2) By focusing for shorter periods of time, you will have more "bookends" to your studying. You will remember more material at the start and end of a study session. By providing more starts and stops in a given period of time, you will retain more information.

This technique is really helpful when you are trying to squeeze some studying in while you have some downtime on call, or when you want to get some studying in before you go home for the day.

7. Make the most of your time.

Your time is precious, especially when you are a resident. Any time that you can carve out to study for your exams is golden. If you have a busy household, then study at a coffee shop on the way home, so that when you are home, you are present for your family and friends.

Check out my post on "Studying on the Move" on my website AnesthesiaMadeEasy.com/onthemove to learn about some techniques and resources.

8. Take advantage of the opportunities given to you by your residency.

Try to attend every lecture and preread for them if you know what the topic will be. These are great opportunities that you will not get after you graduate. Definitely take advantage of the Applied board practice sessions on every chance you get.

9. Target your studying.

When you are on your ICU month, study ICU stuff and when you are on OB, do OB anesthesia reading and questions. If you coordinate your study topics with your rotation, the information will stick with you. You will be using the information while you are studying, which will help you become a better anesthesiologist. Be efficient but reasonable. There will be some rotations that will be so crazy busy that you will only be able to study just enough for the cases you have the next day.

10. Take one day off a week.

Build in one day a week to not be a resident, if possible. Take at least one day a week to not study, preferably on a day off from training. This gives you more time to decompress from your studies. When the day is over, get back to your scheduled routine like a beast.

6

Studying for the Advanced Exam after Graduation

AFTER RESIDENCY GRADUATION you will be doing one of two things:

1. Starting a job
2. Starting a fellowship

You will know if you are headed into the workforce or headed for more training in a fellowship well before you graduate. You will also know if you will have to start the next stage of your life directly after gradation or if you will be given the opportunity to start after the Advanced exam.

No matter which option is available, you will need to build some structure into the time you have, or before you know it, you will be taking the Advanced exam. You will either be well prepared, or wished you had spent more time in preparation.

What works well to prepare for the Advanced Exam?

You will be using the same study methods to prepare for the Advanced exam that you used to successfully take the ITE and pass the Basic exam. The graduates I have spoken to who have been successful on the Advanced exam tend to mix reading, focused study, and practice questions during their study time.

The strategy, tactics, and methods described in chapters 4 and 5 should serve you well for the Advanced exam.

A word of caution

There may be some anesthesia groups/fellowship programs that will go a little easier on you when you are getting ready for the Advanced exam. Your schedule may be a little lighter, you might not have to take calls right away, or you might be given time in the afternoons to go and study. These groups tend to be the exception to the rule.

Many groups/fellowship programs will not give you any slack because you are either the new guy/gal or you are a new fellow.

Why would you not be given some time to study for the Advanced exam?

The expectation from many groups/fellowships is that you have had three years to "study" for the Advanced exam. You have been hired into an anesthesiology group to work or into a fellowship to receive further training. Fellowships only have a year to train you, and if you spend one of your twelve months preparing for the Advanced exam, you have essentially shortened your advanced training by a month.

Should you take a study month?

If you are given the opportunity to start your job or fellowship after the Advanced exam, then take it. You will not regret that decision.

It will give you time to study, relax, and take a breather from being a resident. If you are worried about having a month or two without a paycheck, then plan for this and **save up some money to cover your living expenses while you study for the exam**. You will never again get the opportunity to take some time to concentrate on preparing for an exam.

Ye be warned, me Matey!

If you are given the opportunity to take time off and you choose not to take the time off, don't expect your group or fellowship to go easy on you. In their minds, they gave you the opportunity to study, and you turned it down. You are committed to starting before the exam.

If you are given some extra slack even after turning down the study month, great. Take them up on it. But don't expect it, because you may be very disappointed.

Plan your study month

Don't plan on doing three years of studying in one month. The more you prep **before** you start the study time, the better you will use that time. You can do an in-depth review, but you should not be learning new material.

Everything should be planned out before you start your month.

What areas do you need to focus on?

- You should know your strengths and weaknesses based on your keywords from your previous ITE and the feedback from the Basic exam.

What resources will you use?

- What review books are you going to use?
- Are you going to take a review course during this time?
- What question bank are you going to use?
- Include both reading and practice questions in your study plan.

- If you are looking for some ideas, you can stop by my website: AnesthesiaMadeEasy.com/abaexambooks

Will you be starting your job/fellowship before you take the Advanced exam?

- This is one of the biggest determinants of how you will spend your time in July getting ready for the Advanced Exam.
- What study schedule are you going use? (I have given you some options below.)

Build midweek and weekly goals

- The month of July will fly by before you know it.
- By having midweek and weekly goals, it will help you stay on track of your studying.
- You should have a study plan together for what you will read and which questions you will be doing.

Studying during your new job or fellowship

If you do not have the opportunity to start your job/fellowship training after the Advanced exam, then you need to be studying for the Advanced exam during the end of your CA-3 year. A bulk of your preparation and study should be done during your residency, when you are still in a protected environment.

Talk with your employer or fellowship to find out what kind of schedule to expect, so you can build out how you are going to study. Make sure they know your exam date, so that call schedules and cases can be appropriately covered.

Some groups are somewhat understanding of having you take a lighter schedule to study for the Advanced exam. If you are in a group such as this, consider yourself fortunate. If you are in a group where you are working long hours, then take some time to carve out studying for the exam.

Some guidelines to help you with your studying while you are working

1. Study for thirty minutes in the morning. No matter what happens to your schedule during the day, you will have accomplished some test preparation.

2. When you finish your work for the day, instead of heading straight home, stop by the library, a coffee shop, or a restaurant to get in some studying. By doing this, you will make studying another aspect of your job and will not get distracted when you get home at the end of the day.

3. Consider spending some time studying as a "night cap." Review what you studied during the day and what you need to concentrate on the next day.

4. If you don't have time for a night cap, take five minutes to plan out what you need to study the next day, so that your thirty minutes in the morning will be most helpful.
5. Integrate the questions that you take with the reading you are doing. Your time is tight, so you will have to maximize reinforcing the material every chance you get.
6. Utilize the weekends to study, burn off stress, and rest up. Taking one day off from studying each week will help give you a breather. (If you feel like you can't take a whole day off, then take one afternoon off, without guilt. You might choose to take a day off studying during the week if you are feeling a little burnt out.)

Studying during your "study month"

If you are fortunate enough to start your job or fellowship after the Advanced exam, make the most of it. It is easy to "waste" the month, because you feel like you have so much time to study for the exam. This month will fly by for you as well.

When I took a month off between residency and fellowship to study for the "Advanced Exam,"[1] I made studying my job for that month. I had a systematic approach to my studying, because I knew the month had to count. I knew the best

---

1 I was in the old two-test system of just written and oral exams.

chance I had at passing the Advanced exam was while I was a full-time student again.

The schedule that I loved and worked well for me is as follows:

During the work week (Monday through Friday) I would wake up, have breakfast with the family, then start my reading based on where I was in my review book. I would then eat lunch at home and drive to a coffee shop where I would bribe myself with expensive coffee to take practice questions and review the answers until 4.00 p.m. or 5.00 p.m. I made sure the questions I did at the coffee shop would reinforce the information I was reading in the morning. It was an effective way to study for the exam.

The evenings were spent with my family, and I made sure I got plenty of rest.

On Saturday I would study or do questions in the morning and take the afternoon off. I made Sunday a complete rest day from studying and got some exercise in to relieve stress.

The study schedule above worked well for me, but it might not work well for you. Come up with a plan, try it out, and change the plan as you go along if you need to. The point of having a plan is to go into this time with a road map to get the most out of the time.

Some guidelines to help you with your studying during your study month

1. Make studying for the Advanced exam your job for the month. Set up a schedule and stick to it. It is far

easier to burn through a study month that is unstructured than one where you have set up a schedule.

2. If you are having trouble studying at home, then go to a library, coffee shop, or restaurant to keep you from being distracted.

3. At the end of your study day, do a quick recap of what you studied that day and what you need to study the next day.

4. Integrate your practice questions with your reading so that your reading gets reinforced.

5. Take one day off a week from studying. No reading, no questions, no studying at all. You need breaks to keep burnout at bay.

Conclusion

Graduating from residency is an exciting time in your life. Plan out your studying for the Advanced exam as you prepare for the next season of your life. The better your planning for the July after your graduation, the better your studying will go. Consider doing more preparation during the last few months of residency, especially if you have to start a new job or fellowship before you take the Advanced exam.

Section Three

Graduating from Residency

MOST RESIDENTS GRADUATE from residency without any issues. They show up at their clinical assignments, work hard, are well read, and meet all their requirements. (With the new ABA exams, you have to also pass the ABA Basic exam that we talked about in chapter 3.)

As an anesthesiology resident, you expect that if you follow your rotation schedule, you will get the rotations and case numbers you need for graduation from residency. You expect that "someone" is looking out for you: your chief residents, your rotation director, your program director, or department Chair.

This is a dangerous position to take.

It is ultimately up to you to keep track of your progress. You need to take personal responsibility for your residency training, which will ultimately allow you to become board certified. You don't want to have to extend your residency needlessly because you were not paying attention to case numbers. You need to be proactive in your training to make sure that you graduate on time.

The more you know about what it takes to fulfill the requirements for graduation, the more you can advocate for yourself. Let us walk through the rules, knowledge, strategies, tactics, and skills that will help you get through residency (as smoothly as possible).

7

Learn the Rules to Graduate from Residency

IN REALITY, MOST of these rules are common sense, and most residents learn them on their own. I wanted to include them here to help you avoid any missteps in your training.

There are three main things that will help you get through residency and set you up to graduate on time.

1. Learn the bureaucracy.

You are probably aware that your program is accredited by the American Council on Graduate Medical Education (ACGME). But during residency, you hear about the Anesthesiology Residency Review Committee (RRC) and their rules, and the American Board of Anesthesiology (ABA) and their rules. What do the ACGME, the RRC, and the ABA have to do with each other?

A lot.

The ACGME is the **accreditation organization** in the United States for Graduate Medical Education (GME). GME programs are called internships, residency, and fellowships. Because of the wide variety in medical specialties, the ACGME relies on guidance for each practice-specialty through a specialty-specific Residency Review Committee (RRC). The anesthesiology RRC, with the oversight of the ACGME, determines the rules under which the accredited anesthesiology programs operate and what is required of residents to graduate.

The ABA is the **certifying organization** that sets the standards for anesthesiology board certification. The ABA also has requirements regarding your training.[2]

For anesthesiology board certification, you will have to not only satisfactorily graduate from an ACGME-approved residency but also pass three different exams during and after your training, as we discussed in chapter 3.

During your training, your program will be in contact with the ACGME (usually through the RRC), and the ABA, by submitting reports and documenting that your performance is satisfactory.

---

2 In addition to the primary anesthesiology board certification, the ABA offers several different certifications through its organization: anesthesiology, pain management, hospice and palliative care, pediatric anesthesiology, critical care medicine, and sleep medicine.

What about the American Society of Anesthesiologists (ASA)?

The American Society of Anesthesiologists (ASA) is the national educational and political organization for American anesthesiologists.

I recommend that you join the ASA as a resident, so that you can stay up-to-date on what is happening in our specialty on a national level. There are a handful of benefits that come with membership, in crusading the journal *Anesthesiology* and the *ASA Monitor*.

You can join the ASA as a resident for a reduced rate, which is currently twenty-five dollars a year.

2. Learn the requirements for graduation.

The rules for residency graduation are clearly written down and can be found on the ACGME website. There are general requirements (required by all ACGME programs) and anesthesiology-specific requirements (determined by the Anesthesiology RRC). These rules include the required numbers of rotations, case numbers, and procedures that you need to document to graduate from residency. You will also have some other graduation requirements such as completing a scholarly activity and passing the ABA Basic exam.

There is also a maximum number of days per year that you can spend away from training without having to make up the time, which is set by the ABA. Currently, you can only spend twenty days a year way from residency before having to make up the time.

You can find a link to the anesthesiology requirements through the links at AnesthesiaMadeEasy.com/ACGME.

3. Stay off the radar of the Clinical Competency Committee (CCC) and Professionalism Committee (PC).

The CCC reviews each resident's progression through training and reviews any issues that need to be addressed such as the following:

1. Academic risk—not doing well on ITE exams or failing the ABA Basic exam
2. Concerns of clinical competence—those residents who have weak skills in the OR
3. Professionalism issues—those residents who are brought up in the Professionalism Committee

The PC reviews issues of professionalism such as the following:

1. Not showing up on time
2. Not completing duty hour logs or other paperwork on time
3. Being a disruptive physician (You never want this title.)
4. Being an impaired physician; this is one of the biggest reasons that anesthesiology residents have to extend residency or do not complete training

With these rules in place, you can focus on the strategies/tactics/skills that you need to master to graduate from residency in the following chapters.

8

The Strategies/Tactics of Graduating from Residency

THE FOUR MAIN strategies for you need to graduate from your residency-training program are shown below:

1. Tracking your Rotations, Cases, and Procedures
2. Meeting with your program director regularly
3. Planning your scholarly activity requirement
4. Staying off the radar for the CCC and Professionalism Committee

These four broad areas are relatively easy to achieve because of the way that residency-training programs are designed. Learning the strategies and tactics that follow will keep your training on the rails and keep you headed toward graduation.

1. Tracking your cases, procedures, and rotations

A lot of planning goes into residency rotation schedules and last-minute changes to accommodate your graduation requirements may not be possible. It may be easier for your residency and more painful for you to extend your residency by a month or two.

A. **Download the latest requirements** from the ACGME website so that you will know exactly what is required of you. (ACGME.org)

   • **Rotations:** What are the requirements for your rotations? How many ICU months, how many pediatric rotations, how many OB rotations? Keep track of your rotations so that you meet all these requirements.

   • **Case numbers:** What are the requirements for types of cases? How many general anesthetics? How many spinal anesthetics? How many C-sections? How many cardiac pump cases? How many patients less than three months of age? This is where you will most likely get into trouble. You end up going on vacation, being away from residency for maternity/paternity leave, or you end up on service during a slow month. No matter the cause, you might need more cases to meet the required minimal numbers.

- **Procedure numbers:** What are the requirements for types of procedures? How many central lines, arterial lines, epidurals, etc.

B. **Keep your case logs up-to-date at all times**.

We have all been hammered with the cliché "If you didn't document it, it didn't happen." It holds true for your procedure and case logs, too.

Make sure you keep up your case logs so that you can prove that you completed the requirements. If you lack required cases, then you need to try and fix the issue before you go to your next rotation. If you need to be scheduled an additional month on a rotation, it is better to let your program know early, so that you will not have to extend your residency. You don't want to extend your training in order to get your required case numbers. More importantly, up-to-date case logs can highlight the need for another rotation (if need be) to make sure you get your numbers.

Many hospitals now ask for a copy of your final case log numbers during the credentialing process. Therefore, it is important to make sure that you continue to log all cases, even after you have met the minimum requirements.

Clearly there will be overlap between these areas. For instance, when you do a cardiac pump case, you will more than likely be on a cardiac rotation, doing pump case, and placing central lines and arterial lines. Document every procedure on every case.

2. Meet with your program director regularly

This is an excellent opportunity to review your rotation schedule, case/procedure logs to make sure they are adequate. Practically speaking, case numbers are more than just "numbers"; they are a measure of proficiency. If you have your "numbers," but you are not comfortable with a procedure, then advocate to get some more time on a rotation where you can master the skill. This is one of the few times in your life you will be in a mode of training; take advantage of it.

You will also want to talk about your scholarly activity. (See below.)

3. Planning and documenting your scholarly activity

You must participate in a scholarly activity during your residency. Usually Grand Rounds, published journal articles, abstracts presented at national or regional meetings, quality improvement projects, and presentations at conferences can count toward this requirement. Talk with your program director to find out how most residents fulfill this and when they normally complete it. You may have to adjust when you are going to do it, based on your rotation schedule or planned extended leave, if this is something that will affect you.

Don't wait until you are a CA-3 to think about your scholarly activity. Even if most of the residents in your program do their activity during their CA-3 year, try to get yours completed earlier to get the requirements completed.

4. Staying off the radar of the CCC and Professionalism Committee

When I started as a CA-1, my chief resident gave me the advice: "Stay low, keep moving forward." This keeps you off the radar and keeps you focused on the goal of graduating from residency. If you are deemed as "unsatisfactory" by either the CCC or PC, you may not be able to graduate. To stay off the radar, there are five areas to consider:

1. Perception is reality.

Your reputation as an anesthesiology resident starts on the first day of your residency. "First impressions are lasting impressions" and are difficult to overcome.

You will be judged on not only your personal skills, but your clinical skills as well.

If you get the tag of being "lazy," "unconcerned," or "careless," it can be a hard thing to overcome.

Sometimes anesthesiology takes some acting. Even if you are not an expressive person and tend to have a flat affect, you will need to learn how to "show" your staff you are concerned. You have to "look" concerned and "look" engaged.

I know it is not fair, but this will serve you well when you are working with surgeons who like their anesthesiologists to look engaged and well organized. If you are working with someone who is paranoid, be extra vigilant. If you are working with someone who is laid back, you can still be vigilant but be less uptight.

Part of showing you are engaged is a well-organized anesthesia table will convey a well-organized mind. Work to improve your clinical skills (see chapter 9) so that you will be perceived as a strong resident.

Show up on time to lectures and for the OR. For the love of all that is good, don't be late. If it takes you multiple alarms to get up in the morning, make it happen. If you get tagged as the "oversleeper" you may end up on the docket for the CCC or the PC.

Part of the challenge is getting prepared for the operating room. You can stop by AnesthesiaMadeEasy.com/or-ready to find resources and tips to help you transition into the OR easier.

2. Maintain your didactic pursuits.
There are three main areas for you to concentrate on:

1. USMLE
2. ITE
3. ABA Basic exam

In most programs, you will need to pass USMLE/COMLEX Step 3 to graduate.

You want to do well on your ITE each year. While it is not a requirement to score a certain level, it is a good predictor for future success on the Basic, Advanced, and Applied exams.

We talked about the ABA Basic exam in Section #2. Needless to say, it is one of the roadblocks that can keep you from graduating from residency. No one can force you to study. You need to build your own study program (see chapter 5) to crush these exams. You can also refresh your memory of the article I wrote on our website at AnesthesiaMadeEasy. com/on-the-move.

3. Keep your paperwork up-to-date.

There are some documentation requirements that you will need to maintain to stay off the radar. Some of these requirements are needed to keep you credentials at a hospital.

- Keep both your case log and duty hours documentation up-to-date (as we discussed above).
- Complete your faculty/rotation evaluations on time.
- Make sure you stay current with online training required by the various hospitals at which you rotate. You may not realize how important this is until you get an e-mail from your program director with your department Chair carbon copied on it. This could also cause you to lose your credentials. (See losing your hospital credentials in the next section.)

4. Maintain your medical license and other needed paperwork.

When you started residency, you probably had a Physician In Training (PIT) permit to practice medicine, and you used the hospital's DEA number to write for controlled substances. (Every time you give a narcotic in the OR, you are essentially writing a prescription, filling it, and administering it to the patient.)

Once you obtain your own medical license and DEA numbers, it is up to you to maintain them. (Some residents get a full license so they can moonlight.) It is costly to maintain them, but once you have your own license and DEA numbers, you will need to keep them current. If you let them lapse, then you will not be able to practice as a resident and you will lose your privileges.

Not good.

Losing your hospital privileges

Not only will this be a big headache for you in the future, you will need to disclose any lapses on every application for privileges at every hospital at which you want to work. You may get reported to the ABA, and this becomes something that will follow you for your career.

Consider adding a yearly reminder on your calendar to review your license. These agencies typically send you a single reminder notice by e-mail or through traditional mail. It you move, it is important that you update your information in their files. It is easy to forget when you are busy juggling work, family, and life.

5. Specific advice for special circumstances

Anesthesiology is a small specialty. Keep an open mind and continue to stay a learner throughout the process. You have come back to train in anesthesiology. You have just three years to learn all that you can about this field. Not only do you want to train well, you also want to improve your chances of getting a job when you graduate. You never know who your faculty know outside your institution and how they can help or hinder your ability to find a job after training.

If you are a resident starting anesthesiology after being in a different specialty

Anesthesiology resident training is a challenge for anyone. Even more so for those residents who were in a different specialty before coming to anesthesiology.

You are going to have to perform better than average to "stay off the radar." Anesthesiology faculty may assume you know more than you do, because this is your second training program.

One of the missteps that many residents make when coming to anesthesiology is to make statements like, "In EM, we would intubate this way," or "In IM, we would work the patient up this way." There are many different ways to practice medicine. If your faculty is asking you to do a procedure or work up a certain way, "go with the flow" so long as it doesn't jeopardize patient safety. Now is your time to learn how an anesthesiologist thinks and how they move. We work and communicate differently than other specialties.

If you are asked how it was done in your specialty, absolutely let them know. You might be asked how you would treat a certain disease process, how to do a physical exam on a child, or how you would decide on ventilator management.

My best advice is to stay humble, learn all you can about anesthesiology, and show your faculty that you joined anesthesiology to be an anesthesiologist.

If you are returning to training after being out in practice

Much like a resident who is changing specialties, your program will expect a lot of you.

You have a lot to offer from the training you have already completed and the real-world experience you bring to the table. There are some attending physicians-turned-residents who do well when they come back to get additional training in anesthesiology—and others who do not do well.

Besides the monetary challenges of coming back to training, you will also face the humbling experience of going back to being a resident. (It may not be unusual to have faculty anesthesiologists who are younger than you are.)

Like the residents coming from a different specialty, you have much to offer to your training program.

If you came back to training after being out, then the best advice I can give you is to "embrace the suck." There will be some things that really suck about coming back. If you keep your eye on the goal of completing residency and getting back to practicing medicine, you can make it through.

When you are called upon for your expertise, then by all means show them what you have to offer.

9

Skills to Graduate from Residency

I PUT THIS section in for completeness. Most residents have no trouble with the acquisition of clinical skills. If you are early in your clinical anesthesia years, this section will be more helpful for you. Feel free to read, skim, or skip this section depending on your level of training.

There are few things as satisfying as being able to intubate a patient after a room full of people could not, sinking a pulmonary artery catheter introducer, or placing an outstanding block on a patient with ultrasound. These are the outward skills for which anesthesiologists are known, and they are part of the reason why you went into anesthesiology in the first place. Knowing how to develop these skills is important for your development as an anesthesiologist.

Some of these skills will be improved by your anesthesiology knowledge, but they will all be improved by consciously taking the time to learn and practice them.

Getting good at building your clinical skills will help you as an anesthesiologist, and it will also help you to graduate.

Developing your clinical skills

There are seven concepts that I have found to improve anesthesiology resident procedural skills acquisition:

1. Slow is smooth; smooth is fast.

I love the US Navy SEALs saying of "Slow is smooth, smooth is fast." It holds well for SEALs on the shooting range and will hold well for you.

When you are doing procedures, take some time and slow down. Work on your technique and don't worry about being fast. Getting faster will come with time. By developing and having good technique, the speed will come much easier than having sloppy technique and just trying to go faster.

A good example is with intubations. When you take your time and slow down just a little as you are putting the laryngoscope blade in the mouth, advancing the blade to get a view, and putting the endotracheal tube through the vocal cords, you will ultimately find yourself getting faster.

2. Become well versed in different types of equipment.

While not required for board certification, knowing how to use different blades, fiber-optic scopes, video laryngoscopes, and ultrasound machines will help you when you graduate.

There are required skills you need to document to graduate, but there are other skills that you need to master to become a confident anesthesiologist. It will also add to the perception of you being a professional.

3. Once you hone your skills using a certain technique, try doing it differently.

For example, let's say you get really good at placing sitting epidurals. It takes you ten minutes from sitting up until the patient rests comfortably through her next contraction. Now is the time to learn how to place the epidural while the patient is in lateral position. You never know when this technique will come in handy. Experience with a wide array of tools will likely give you more flexibility and comfort wherever you work. Look for ways to get Maximal Resident Benefit (MRB). MRB is finding ways to get the most learning from each case. Even if you don't have to use a fiber-optic scope to manage an airway, you may have decided to use to get better at the technique.

4. Learn to use equipment when it is easy.

The time to use new equipment is not when things are difficult. You need to get comfortable with using equipment when the situation is not dire or difficult so that you know how to use it properly.

The time to learn how to use the video laryngoscope is when the patient has an easy airway—not when you are having trouble. You first need to master the skill when it is easy, then you will know how to utilize it when the situation becomes difficult.

5. Keep a well-organized anesthesia space.

Be organized and keep your work station clean. Attention to detail will get you far in this area. When you look confident and well organized for procedures, whether it's intubation, A-lines, central lines, and so on, you will instill the sense that you are competent to your staff.

This will do two things for you: (a) It will garner confidence from your surgeon and your staff when they look at your space and it looks meticulous and well organized. (b) When an emergency happens, it will be easy for you and your staff to find your medications and equipment.

6. Present patients to your staff in an organized manner.

Your first interaction with your staff for a specific case will happen the night before, when you call him/her to discuss the cases for the next day. This is a great opportunity to show your staff what you have to offer. An added benefit is that it helps you practice organizing your thoughts in a clear and concise manner, a skill that will pay dividends during the SOE of the Applied exam (see chapter 15).

You don't want to appear unprepared for your day. If you get the reputation of being unprepared, your faculty will remember that when it comes time for letters of recommendation.

7. Take simulation practice seriously.

Simulation training is a good opportunity to be able to practice skills in a safe environment. Hopefully, as we inch closer to having an OSCE on the Applied exam, more residency programs will be adding this skills training to the curriculum. If offered, take every opportunity to go to the simulation lab.

Section Four

Passing Your Applied Exam

THIS LAST OBJECTIVE, "Completing Your Board Certification" is dependent on the other two objectives: "Doing Well on Your Exams" and "Graduating from Residency."

Once you graduate from residency, you have two more steps:

1. Passing the ABA Advanced exam
2. Passing the ABA Applied exam:
    a. Standardized Oral Examination (SOE)
    b. Objective Structured Clinical Examination (OSCE)

These two exams are where most people get fouled up.

They push off studying for the Advanced exam until after graduation (because they have senioritis), and they push off studying for the Applied exam because they feel like they have to pass the Advanced exam before studying for the Applied exam.

While it makes sense to study for only one exam at a time, I would suggest practicing some of the skills for the Applied exam as you are preparing for the other exams. The more practice you get at taking oral exams the better off you will be. (We will talk about this in chapters 15.)

The good news is the strategy, tactics, and skills that you used to prepare for the ITE and the ABA Basic exam can be used to prepare for the ABA Advanced exam. There is the challenge of studying while you are getting ready to graduate and starting a new job or fellowship. I have laid out some strategies and tactics about how to tackle these challenges in chapter 6.

Many residents avoid taking extra practice exams during residency because they are intimidating and they do not want to appear "foolish." They reality is that they are actually foolish not to utilize a resource at a time when it is readily available.

10

Learning to Play a New Game

Yes, it is an oral exam. It could be worse...it could be a rectal exam.

—ME (JUST NOW)

THERE IS A wide variety in the amount of exam preparation that residencies give to their residents. Your residency may be one that spends a lot of time prepping you for the ABA Applied exam or you may have to do a lot of your preparation on your own.

Even if you're in a residency that does not spend a lot of time prepping for the exam, you can still have a good chance at passing it the first time.

That is your goal.

Unfortunately, most anesthesiology residents think of the Applied exam like an exam to study for after they have passed the other exams. (I thought the same way when I was a resident.) Sure, they do some mock orals during residency and/or fellowship, but the bulk of their preparation for the Applied exam is after graduating from residency and passing the Advanced exam.

But you are not like "most residents," are you?

If you use the integrated approach described in this book, you will be prepping for the Applied exam for years before you even sign up for the exam.

Do yourself a favor and start practicing for the Applied exam during your CA-1 year. I will give you some guidelines in putting it all together starting in chapter 33 but start preparing for the Applied exam early in your training.

Why does the Applied Exam cause so much angst?

Residents seem to be waiting until the last moment to start their preparation for the Applied exam. Part of the reason for this procrastination is the angst that the Applied exam creates.

The angst caused by the Applied exam comes from three main areas:

1. Lack of experience with oral exams
   We do few oral exams in the United States during our medical training. We do get "pimped" during our training, but the way we answer in slang, jargon, and

incomplete sentences does not prepare us for the exam. It is also during these pimp sessions that we are given feedback in the form of facial expressions and head nods (neither of which should happen during the Applied exam). What we don't get is the type of formalized grading that you would get in a real oral board exam.

2. The oral boards have such a lore about them that they become larger than life.

   Just about every anesthesiologist has some great story around their oral exam. One of your faculty had Miller, Barash, Chestnut, or Cote as an examiner; or their luggage was lost, and they almost had to take the exam in sweatpants; or they just barely got through all the questions before time was up; or the "smartest resident you ever knew" a couple of classes before you failed the exam.

3. The OSCE has recently been added to the Applied exam. There is a good chance that you have studied for and passed OSCE in the past. This is still a new part of the Applied exam and the ABA is still trying to figure out how to administer this exam itself. With proper preparation, this part of the OSCE should not be a stumbling block for you.

What does lack of experience and lore of the exam do?

Because the Applied exam has been built up so much, some residents are paralyzed with fear. Many residents are "just trying to get through residency," and they may also procrastinate their "oral board" preparation as long as possible.

They treat the Applied exam like a totally separate exam, when the same knowledge base gained during the Basic and Advanced exams will be used on the Applied exam.

Residents race off to take Applied exam review courses in an effort to get ready for the exam. But in so doing they are trying to acquire new strategies they have never used before at the very last minute.

They tend to rely heavily on anesthesia knowledge and luck to pass the Applied exam. Not good.

Your best shot at passing the Applied exam is to pass it the first time. Every time you have to retake it, statistically, your chances of passing go down.
The object of the Applied exam is to be scored by four board-certified anesthesiologists such that you pass the exam. This will be the most challenging exam of your career, but it is passable. With proper preparation, you can pass the Applied exam on the first try.

Time to learn a new game
The good news is the anesthesia knowledge you have gained throughout your anesthesia training will be put to good use. The hours studying, taking exams, and answering questions

in the operating room will prepare you for your Applied exam.

However, for the Applied exam, you will have a completely new set of objectives, rules, strategy, tactics, and skills to master. You also have a new set of expectations because of the nature of the exam.

Many residents try and learn this new game after completing the written exams and residency. However, as I will show you in chapter 25 through chapter 29, you can integrate these things into your residency so that you know how to play the game long before you land in North Carolina[3] to take your exam.

The Applied Exam has changed.

If you complete your residency training on or after October 1, 2016 (which is probably most of you), you will have two major sections to the Applied exam:

1. Standardized Oral Examination (SOE)
   The SOE is the part of the Applied Exam that is the old "oral exam," which we will go into greater detail in the next chapter.
2. Objective Structured Clinical Examination (OSCE)

---

3 Every Applied exam is now given at the ABA testing site in North Carolina.

This section is relatively new. I go into great detail about the OSCE in chapter 11. I also have resources for you at AnesthesiaMadeEasy.com/OSCE.

11

The Objective Structured Clinical Exam (OSCE) Rules

Background

A s discussed in chapter 10, the Applied exam will now consist of both the Objective Structured Clinical Examination (OSCE) and the Standardized Oral Examination (SOE), which we will discuss in chapter 14. Unfortunately, we all thought that the OSCEs were behind us with the USMLE/ COMLEX Step 2. It looks as if you will have to face it again. OSCEs are considered "low-fidelity simulations," and they have specific objectives that will be tested at various stations.

Who will be taking the OSCE?

The ABA OSCE is scheduled to be launched in March 2018. Residents who graduate from residency on or after October 1, 2016, will take this part of the Applied exam. It is also quite possible that if examinees fail the Advanced or Applied exams enough times, they may also be included within the group to take the OSCE.

How you will be graded on the OSCE?

The grading for the OSCE will be separate and distinct from the SOE. If you fail one and pass the other, you only have to retake the section that you failed.

I would assume that some of the core principles involved in grading the SOE (anesthesia knowledge, adaptability, judgment, and communication) will be used on the OSCE as well.

If the OSCE is graded like the SOE, you will need to amass a certain number of points to pass. In the OSCE detailed content outline, it regularly states "the successful candidate will demonstrate the following behaviors:" I would think that if you touch on the points that follow this statement for each section, you should be able to obtain a passing score for the OSCE section.

OSCE organization

When the OSCE is administered, it will either be before or after the SOE, which will make for a long day. The OSCE consists of seven stations. In between each OSCE, you will have four minutes to transition to the next station and review a brief regarding the clinical situation you are expected to manage. At each station, you will have eight minutes to complete the specific skill on which you are being tested. There are two types of stations at which you will be tested:

1) Communication skill stations: You might talk with a standardized patient about a complication, discuss canceling a case with a surgeon, consent a patient for a procedure, or a variation of the above.

2) Technical skill stations: You might be asked to interpret ultrasound images of vascular access or anatomy for an ultrasound block, review an echocardiogram, or interpret hemodynamic variables on a monitor.

In chapter 12, we will discuss some strategies, tactics, and expectations of the OSCE. In chapter 13, we will go on to explore some OSCE skills that will help you navigate the waters of the ABA OSCE.

12

OSCE Strategies, Tactics, and Expectations

Knowing is half the battle.

—G. I. JOE

BECAUSE THE ADDITION of the OSCE is so new to the ABA board certification process, there is still much debate about what the OSCE will look like. To be honest, this chapter was the most challenging one to write. The ABA OSCE is still so new, it will be somewhat of a challenge to prepare for it. I will continue to update my webpage as new information becomes available at AnesthesiaMadeEasy.com/ OSCE.

OSCE strategies and tactics

Chances are you have already taken an OSCE for your USMLE/COMPLEX Step 2 exams, so taking another OSCE, while stressful, will not be entirely new to you. The ABA has given you an outline of what they will be testing. Your key strategy to prepare for the ABA OSCE should be to review the OSCE content outline and make sure you can address each of the points under each section, which states "The successful candidate will demonstrate the following behaviors." The more behaviors you can demonstrate during the exam, the more points you will accumulate and the closer you will get to passing.

As discussed in chapter 11, the ABA OSCE is divided into two major sections: 1. Communication and Professionalism and 2. Technical skills. You will be using your anesthesia knowledge, communication, adaptability, and flexibility, along with your motor skills, to pass these stations. Review the detailed OSCE outline to find out exactly what they will be looking for.

Just as an oral board examiner helps navigate you through the oral board by asking questions, I think the standardized patient will have several prompts to initiate a discussion about the objectives that are being tested. Ensure that you listen to and specifically answer the questions that are being asked by that standard patient.

Each one of these sections has its own strategies and tactics.

1. Communication and professionalism strategies and tactics

For the **Communication and professionalism section**, much of your preparation for the SOE will help you in managing these questions. However, you will need to make sure you touch on the talking points that the examiners are looking for. For example, when you are doing informed consent, you will want to explain why they are having the procedure, benefits/risks of the procedure, give them alternatives, and so forth. This will take a little practice, but make sure you touch on all the behaviors they are looking for.

For the Communication and Professionalism stations, you may have any of the following scenarios to manage:

1. You will be **obtaining informed consent** from a patient. The examiners will be grading you based on your interaction with a standardized patient. There are a number of things they will be looking for, such as communicating on the level of the patient and doing a complete informed consent. Ensure that you include risks, benefits, and alternatives to any procedure being discussed.

2. You will be **discussing treatment options** with a patient. You will be analyzing a clinical scenario and coming up with treatment options and then discussing them with the simulated patient.

3. You will have to deal with a **periprocedural complication**. You will need to evaluate a periprocedural complication, come up with a plan to deal with it, and discuss this plan with a standardized patient. Have some complication algorithms in place to deal with common issues like ulnar nerve injury, vision loss following prone spine surgery, and MH crisis.

4. You will have **ethical issues** to address. This is the one part in the OSCE content outline that is exceedingly vague. It directs you to read The ASA Guideline for the Ethical Practice of Anesthesiology. (You can find the article through our link at AnesthesiaMadeEasy. com/OSCE.)

5. You will have to **communicate with other professionals.** This section will probably be very similar to how you would answer questions for the SOE (see chapter 15).

6. You will be demonstrating practice-based learning and improvement. This section deals with patient safety and quality improvement based on a clinical scenario. There is not much guidance on this one either. Perhaps you will be asked about beta blockers, or Surgical Care Improvement Project (SCIP) measures like prophylactic antibiotics or venous thromboembolism

prophylactics. Reviewing The Joint Commission SCIP measures would probably be a prudent thing to do.

2. Technical skills strategies and tactics

For the **technical skills section**, you will need to review lots of pictures and videos of monitors, echoes, and ultrasound. This seems overwhelming but don't make it so. There are only so many things you can be asked during the OSCE, and they are all listed on the OSCE content outline.

For example, there are eleven views of the transesophageal echo that you will be tested on. Knowing which view to study will help you prepare for the types of questions you will be asked during the OSCE.

The Technical Skills section has three major divisions in it:

1. Interpretation of monitors

   You will be interpreting a value (like a cardiac output), a waveform (like a flow-volume loop), or a value and waveform (like a central venous pressure). The OSCE content outline is very specific in which monitors will be tested and what data (value or waveform) will be tested.

2. Interpretation of echocardiograms

   You will be interpreting basic transesophageal echo images. In these images, you will be asked to view, identify anatomy and make diagnoses/treatment decisions. It might be a picture or video on a computer screen. You should also be prepared to manipulate a probe in a model to obtain the picture that the examiner asks of you.

3. Application of ultrasonography

   You will have to identify ultrasound anatomy related to vascular cannulation and nerve blocks. You might have to use an ultrasound probe on a standardized patient and simulate needle placement. Alternately, you may be given a gel simulator to place a needle in a location under ultrasound guidance. A screenshot of the anatomical region may be taken, and you may be asked to identify anatomical structures on that still image.

OSCE expectations

If we extrapolate from how the ABA grades the SOE, I would assume that the OSCE will be engineered to give you a broad exam of different aspects of anesthesiology.

According to the ABA: "The OSCE is a series of short, simulated clinical situations in which a candidate is evaluated on skills such as history taking, physical exam, procedural skills, clinical decision-making, counseling, professionalism, and interpersonal skills."[4]

---

4 Quoted from "Staged Examinations Policy Book February 2016" found at theaba.org.

13

OSCE Skills You Need to Learn

S OME OF THE skills that you will learn in chapter 15 for the
SOE you will be able to use on the OSCE. The OSCE
is like a collection of grab-bag questions: You will have just
eight minutes at each of the seven stations to assess the situation, move through the scenario, and communicate your
findings/conclusions.

OSCE Skill #1: Get in the mind-set of
playing the part

You will be going through situations where you will have to
"play the part" of an anesthesiologist. You are not an examinee; you are going through the scenarios while being an anesthesiologist. During these ministations, you will be talking
with a standardized patient, colleague, or surgeon. Adjust

your speaking style depending on whom you are interacting with. Make sure to use lay terms when conversing with the standardized patients.

OSCE Skill #2: Ignore the examiners in the room

This can be one of the most unnerving things that you will encounter. An examiner might be in the room as an observer/grader. You will want to focus your attention on the standardized patient. Unless the examiners are asking you questions, act as though they are a medical student shadowing you and keep your focus on the actor with whom you are interacting. Alternatively, there may be a video camera in the room with the examiner watching from another location as you interact with the standardized patient.

OSCE Skill #3: Identifying the OSCE scenario you will be tested on

There are only so many different scenarios you will be tested on—and you know what they are, because you have reviewed the OSCE content outline. Mentally thinking what type of station you are being tested on (monitoring, echo, ultrasound, consenting a patient, etc.) will put you in the mind-set of working through the problem. Clearly identifying the scenario will help you focus. You will be provided a stem giving some insight into the clinical situation prior to entering the

OSCE. You will be allotted approximately four minutes to review the stem.

OSCE Skill #4: Change to the new scenario

Just like when you change from the stem question to the grab-bag questions (see chapter 15), you will need to leave the previous scenario behind when you move to the new one. However you did on the previous section is done. If you continue to return to the previous scenario in your head, then you will miss parts on the current station. Many of us have a tendency to fixate on the questions we get wrong without giving ourselves credit for the ones we get correct. As difficult as it may be, try not to dwell over a difficult OSCE as this can impact your performance on subsequent stations. You want to get as many points as you can on the current station.

OSCE Skill #5: Don't tell; show what you would do

You might be asked to demonstrate getting an ultrasound picture of an interscalene block. You will not be telling the examiner your approach and needle direction, you will be showing it to them. When you are given the opportunity, always show, don't tell what you would do. You don't want to waste precious time with the examiner telling you to show them, don't tell them.

Preparing for the OSCE

Take some time and practice the OSCE questions with your SOE study buddy, focusing on the parts that the ABA have stated "The successful candidate will demonstrate the following behaviors:"

We have devoted chapter 16 to helping you with the strategies, tactics, and skills to help you prepare for the ABA OSCE. We also have a webpage AnesthesiaMadeEasy.com/OSCE that will have the most up-to-date information that comes from the ABA. As new resources become available, we will update the webpage.

14

The Standardized Oral Examination (SOE) Rules

Background

WHEN YOU HEAR your faculty talk about the oral exam or the Applied exam, what they are probably referring to is the Standardized Oral Examination (SOE). This is a major change in how the ABA is administering the exam, so know that some of your faculty may be talking using oral exam, Applied exam, and SOE all interchangeably.

How will you be graded during the SOE?

What are the criteria by which you will be measured during the SOE? The oral examiners will be testing you on four broad areas to determine if you should become a diplomate of the American Board of Anesthesiology.

1. Anesthesia knowledge

- You have to have adequate anesthesiology knowledge. You cannot state "because this is what we did at my university." You have to know the rationale behind the decisions.
- As we were told by my chairman, the ABA wants to test the "breadth and depth" of your knowledge. Will the examiners drill down to the mechanism of Dantrolene?—maybe.
- You have to show both didactic knowledge and clinical knowledge. This is a challenge in an oral exam, but you have to just be smart about how you answer the questions.

2. Adaptability

- You will have to remain flexible and adaptable, because that is what we do every day in the OR.
- Build a plan, but plan for bad stuff to happen.
- Most complications in medicine are predictable, and you can use your anesthesia knowledge to anticipate them.
- You will be asked to talk through scenarios on the exam that you normally would do. The situation will change, and so you will have to adapt to the situation.

3. Judgment

- You will be dealing with a lot of gray areas during your exam.
- You will likely have to prioritize two conflicting issues and make the best judgment you can.
- Even if you are adaptable, you have to use your judgment when you need to stick with your plan and not "adapt" your way into a bad situation.
- There may be times that you have to change the plan because of the patient's condition.

4. Communication

- Answer the question you are asked—not the one you wish you were asked.
- Don't answer a "what do you think?" question with a "what would you do?" answer. Pay attention to what is being asked of you.
- In the OR, you have to communicate well with other physicians, nurses, OR Staff, and patients. In the exam, you will have to communicate not just the how, but the why.
- Your answer must be conveyed in an organized manner.
- Explain yourself like you would to a colleague in a different specialty. (You have to show them that you know what you know.)

- Don't use slang or jargon. Avoid stammering and work to provide a clear, consistent communication.
- Your answers should be thorough but concise. Avoid one word answers. Explain what the issues are and what your concerns are.
- The communication style you use with the oral examiners during the SOE will be different than during your OSCE, where you are speaking with a simulated patient.
- Be concise—say the most possible information to address the situation by using the fewest amount of words.
- Use generic drug names.

SOE organization

The SOE portion of the Applied exam is given over seventy minutes.[5]

During that time, you will have two sessions (thirty-five minutes each) that will each consist of a stem question for twenty-five minutes followed by three small stems (called "grab bag") for ten minutes.

Each session is taken in front of two oral board examiners. Since you have two exam sessions in the same day, you will be sitting in front of a total of four oral board examiners.

- The first session is a long stem. All of the preop information is included, and it is assumed that you are in the OR already. The first session is organized so that you deal with intraop issues/postop issues/grab bag questions.

- The second session is a short stem, because you are going to work up the patient in the preop phase of the surgery. The second session is organized so that you deal with preop issues/intraop issues/grab-bag questions.

- Each set of stem questions and grab-bag questions are intentionally paired together to provide an evaluation of a wide variety of anesthesiology-related topics. For example, if you have a cardiac stem question, you will likely not get any further cardiac topics in your grab-bag scenarios or your second stem question.

---

5 This is assuming no OSCE. When the OSCE is added to the testing, it will make for an even longer day.

Timeline for the SOE portion of the Applied Exam

First stem—long

You will be dealing with intraoperative and postoperative issues.

- Ten-minute prep to dissect the stem in the holding area at the testing site (see chapter 29). This time is not counted in the thirty-five-minute test time. With the new Applied exam in place, they are very strict about the ten-minute prep time. The stem will be given to you on a single piece of paper. You can use this paper to read, underline, and make notes in bulleted fashion. You will not have time to read detailed notes during the SOE, so bulleted points work better. This is your time to organize your thoughts and dissect the stem (see chapter 13, Skill #1). You will then be taken to another room where you will be administered the exam.

- Ten-minute intraoperative section (given by senior examiner)

  The questions are asked from a preselected set of questions, but the examiner may ask others as well.

- Fifteen-minute postoperative section (given by junior examiner)

  The questions are asked from a preselected set of questions, but the examiner may ask others as well.

- Ten-minute grab bag (given by senior examiner)
  Consists of three distinct cases unrelated to the stem question or to each other. You are given one grab-bag case at a time and asked to answer questions about it. The senior examiner will give you the grab-bag questions verbally, you state your answer, then you move on to the next question.

Second stem—short

After you finish the long stem and grab-bag questions, you will then move on to the short stem and grab-bag questions.

You will be dealing with Preoperative and Intraoperative issues

- Ten-minute prep to dissect the stem; again, this stem is on a single piece of paper, and the time is not counted in the "exam" time of the test.
- Ten-minute preoperative section (given by senior examiner)
  The questions are asked from a preselected set of questions, but the examiner may ask others as well.
- Fifteen-minute intraoperative section (given by junior examiner)
  The questions are asked from a preselected set of questions, but the examiner may ask others as well.
- Ten-minute grab bag (given by senior examiner)
  Consists of three unrelated cases; you are given one grab-bag case at a time and asked to answer questions

about it. The senior examiner will give you the grab-bag questions verbally, you state your answer, then you move on to the next question.

In the next chapter, we will dig into the strategy, tactics, and expectations of the SOE.

15

SOE Strategies, Tactics, and Expectations

WHETHER YOU KNOW it or not, you have been preparing for the Applied exam. With every exam you took, every case you did, and every procedure you completed, you were laying the ground work for the Applied exam.

As you get closer to the Applied exam, you should be fine-tuning your knowledge, your speaking skills, and your exam-taking skills.

To prepare for the SOE, you will have to do the following:

1. Set a timeline to prepare for the Applied exam
2. Increase your anesthesia knowledge by continuing to study

3. Learn how to answer questions orally
4. Learn the expectations of the SOE:
    1. What the exam is like?
    2. What the examiners expect from you?
    3. What to expect from the examiners?
    4. What the testing environment will be like?

Set a timeline to study for the exam

Just like your other exams, you can expect to have a baseline of ongoing study, onto which you will add an intensified studying routine, which will increase until you take the exam. You don't want to peak your studying for your Applied exam too early. Do so early and you can burn out. Most examinees I have spoken to, start targeted studying about six months prior to their exam.

Preparation for how to answer questions should start your CA-1 year. Because communication is such a large part of this exam, you should not be "learning" how to do this at the end of your training.

Increase your anesthesia knowledge

You will have to review your anesthesia knowledge. Pick your reference and use it to learn, review, and hone your anesthesia knowledge specifically for the oral boards.

If you choose to take a review course, I recommend taking it three months before the exam, so that you can use the information to brush up and intensify your studying.

I have some recommended resources for you at AnesthesiaMadeEasy.com/abaexambooks.

Learn how to answer questions orally

If your residency puts on mock orals (where you get to practice taking oral exams), participate in every opportunity that you can. If you get to take the practice exam yourself, do it. It is your opportunity to practice. This is the equivalent of doing practice questions for your other exams. By practicing, it will help you study for both the SOE and the OSCE.

This gives you the opportunity to: (1) answer like you would at your Applied Exam, and (2) practice your new Applied skills like how to dissect a stem (chapter 13) and how to anticipate complications.

If, instead, you are asked to play the part of the examiner, then take that opportunity as well. When you are an "oral examiner," use that opportunity to learn how to better take the Applied exam yourself.

When you give mock orals, pay attention to the following:

1. Spend time dissecting the stem yourself. It will give you practice and help you to predict what the questions are going to be about.
2. Once you dissect the stem, look through the questions to see how they are organized and what kinds of questions will be asked.
3. Pay attention to how the examinee answers the question:
   1. What annoys you off as an examiner? (so you don't do it yourself)
   2. Does the examinee have a way to phrase her answers that sounds good?
4. Are there questions or topics that you would not be able to answer if you were an examinee? If so, you just found an area that you need to brush up on.

Learn the expectations of the SOE Exam

Knowing the expectation of the ABA Basic and Advanced exams is pretty intuitive. You were given practice exams in the form of the ITE every year. Because the Applied exam is an oral exam, you will be interacting directly with the examiners, which also brings with it a different set of expectations.

When you know what the examiners expect from you, what to expect from the examiners, and what to expect from the Applied exam itself, you will be able to manage these expectations and take the exam successfully. This will help you in your preparation for the exam, and will help you manage your stress level.

What oral examiners expect from you.

A large part of the Applied Exam is in presentation. You want to behave in a way that the examiners are expecting you to behave. The only thing they know about you when you come into the room is your name. They do not know where you trained, what your ITE scores are, how many times you have taken the Applied exam before—nothing. You want to blend in with all the other examinees so that they do not unintentionally grade you harder than expected.

According to the ABA: "The SOE is an oral assessment using realistic patient cases with two board-certified anesthesiologist examiners questioning an examinee in a standardized manner. These examinations assess clinical decision-making and the application or use of medical knowledge with realistic patient scenarios."[6]

Ten expectations that oral examiners have of you

1. Answer the questions that the examiners ask you.
   • You will want to provide the answer to the question as quickly as possible.

---

6 Quoted from Staged Examinations Policy Book February 2016.

- We will go into greater detail on how to answer questions in the Skills section to follow.
2. You will be expected to have a general working knowledge of all subspecialties in anesthesiology.
   - The point of the stem question and the grab-bag questions will test this.
   - They don't expect you to have done advanced training in everything, so when you reach the point where you are out of your depth, say so. This is especially true of cardiac and pediatric questions.
3. Do not ask questions of the examiners.
   - Unless you respectfully ask them to repeat the question because you didn't hear it, or rephrase the question.
   - Alternately, you can state "Assuming the patient's asthma is well controlled on her current therapy, I would…" This lets the examiners know you did or did not understand the question. The will correct you if you are wrong.
4. Be conservative with your anesthesia management.
   - Don't be cavalier, even if you would be in practice.
   - The oral examiners are trying to judge you to see if you would follow the standard of care.
5. Don't tell them all the stuff **that you could do**, tell them **what you would do and why**.
   - You will need to make a decision and follow through on it.

- They don't want to hear all the possibilities, they want to hear **what you would do**.
- Don't make the examiner ask you "Why?" Tell them straight away.
- Pick a course of action and be confident. For some of the questions, there is no one right answer. Choose the best path and be able to defend it. If/when the patient scenario changes, adjust and move forward.

6. Examine the patient.
   - You will have to talk through how you would do it.
   - You cannot assume they know that you always check breath sounds, or you would examine the airway. You have to let them know you would do it.

7. Eventually you will get to a question you do not know.
   1. Don't freak out.
   2. State "I don't know." or "I cannot recall at this time." or "I would have to review that information."

8. Continue to be flexible.
   - You will make a decision and answer what you would do. The examiners will then change the scenario and see what you would do then. Expect this so that you know it is coming.
   - Sometimes you will be given a scenario where you should not be flexible/adaptable and need

to stay with your decision. This takes a certain amount of panache to pull these off.

9. Speak like a consultant anesthesiologist.
   - Don't use slang or jargon. Don't expect that they know anesthesiology by stating "you know."
   - Speak as if you were explaining your answers to medical school students.

10. They expect you to be confident, but humble.
   - Don't say "in my practice." In the minds of the oral examiners, you have no practice. You have been out of residency for less than a year, so be cautious with trying to tell a seasoned anesthesiologist the best way to do something.

What to expect from oral board examiners

When you know what the interaction might be with the examiners, you will not be surprised, and you can focus on their questions and your answers.

You can expect the examiners to do the following:

1. The only know your name

- The only thing they know is your name. They don't know your ITE, your Basic, or your Advanced exam scores. They don't know where you are from, where you went to school—nothing. They don't know how many times you have taken the exam.

- You have to show them you know the answer by **verbalizing everything**. You cannot assume that they know how you would check your machine, or listen to breath sounds before pulling back a tube, or checking for a disconnect at the Y piece because that is the most likely place it will happen. You have to show them, by telling them, how you would do it in clinical practice.

2. Introduce themselves

- Don't be surprised if they are authors of major anesthesia textbooks.
- If you see me there—just kidding. (You won't see me there, unless it is for the tribunal for writing this insider's guide. Wink, wink, nudge, nudge. Relax. You got this.)

3. Have a junior board examiner and senior board examiner

- Sometimes the senior examiner will appear to be older, sometimes not. The senior examiner will start and close the exam, and the junior examiner will conduct the middle portion.

• Knowing that the senior examiner will be giving the grab-bag questions will help you know how your pace is going. It will also help you know what to expect at the end of the exam.

4. Have their personalities come out only after the introduction and handshake

• All examiners will be cordial during the introductions, and some will be very friendly during the introductions.

• After the introductions, the personalities emerge.

The annoyed: Everything you say seems to annoy the examiner.

The interrupter: You are answering a question, and they interrupt you in the middle of your answer.

The ambivalent: You cannot tell if they like you or not.

The buddy: They smile, sometimes head nod (even though they are not supposed to), and seem happy to have you there.

The coach: They want you to do well and try to help you get through the questions to get you there.

The bored: The examiners are thinking about enjoying the mountains around North Carolina and how great the weather is.

The sleepy: There have been some examiners who have fallen asleep during the exam. Don't freak out.

The famous: These are the examiners who wrote the same textbooks you used to study for the exam. Their personality will not matter because you will be too intimidated to notice.

5. They will interrupt you

- When you get interrupted, stop talking and listen. You have answered the question appropriately, and the examiner is ready to move on. When you are interrupted, don't consider it rude, consider the question answered adequately. You just got points toward winning.

- When you are practicing during your mock orals with a study partner, practice interrupting each other as it can be very unnerving the first few times it happens.

- Do not show any signs of annoyance. You should be happy that you answered the question well enough to move on.

6. Have no body language or verbal feedback when you are giving your answers

They will not smile at you after introductions are made. There will be no head nods, or smiles, or maybe even eye blinks. (Are they still alive?) They are instructed to convey no body language indicating if you are doing well or not.

7. Be intimidating. They might not mean to, but they will.

- No matter how they look (bored, tired, annoyed, aggressive), you need to just keep moving through the exam.
- Stay cool, you have thirty-five minutes with them. Then you get to go to the next room and do it all again.
- Don't expect that they are experts in every subspecialty, but consider that they may be. Some have been doing oral exams for years.

What to expect from the exam itself

When you are taking the exam, there will be some things you are not accustomed to.

1. Expect to have the oral examiners drill down into a topic and see how deep you know the subject.

- If you are doing well, they might see just how deep the rabbit hole goes. They may "drill down" to a receptor level question or until you say "I don't know."
- Don't get too stressed out; that is actually a good sign.

2. Expect that you might not know all the answers.
   - As long as it is not a pattern, you will do OK.

3. Expect the examiners to ask questions that have multiple answers.
   - This is very different than the Basic and Advanced exams where you will select the best answer from a list of answers. You have to come up with your own answer.
   - As long as you have a justification that is sound, you will do fine.

4. Expect that you will make mistakes.
   - Some will be wounding, others may be fatal. If you make a mistake and can correct it right away, do so quickly.
   - If you realize later in the game and are still on the same topic, feel free to amend out the plan and explain why.

5. Expect the examiners to give you a choice between two things and still make you discuss the option you would not choose (see chapter 17—Key Target #3).

6. Expect the questions they ask you to be related to the patient and case described in the stem, unless they state otherwise.

7. Expect the patient is healthy, unless otherwise stated.
   - Remember the patient's past medical history when you are answering your questions.
   - Don't make the case go bad on your own. You have to be told that it will go bad before it does.
   - Don't assume something bad happened, until you are told that it did.

8. Expect the patient to get worse, not better.
   - Your plans will go sideways, airways will fail, plans will fail, you will have to go to your backup of backup plans.
   - Sometimes your patient will die. That isn't necessarily a failing event on the exam. Use your ACLS skills and continue to treat the patient until they tell you to stop.

9. Expect the case will change rapidly.

10. Expect to feel like the primary case will end abruptly, and you will be on to the grab-bag cases. (That's a good thing, because you want to finish the entire section.)

11. When you hear "Let's leave this case and move on to some others," the case is done. Keep moving forward. The grab-bag cases will have nothing to do with the original stem, so forget about it and move forward.

12. They have a list of questions in front of them—if you notice them skipping over questions or abruptly changing topics, you are doing well.
    - You may not always get to the third grab-bag question. I know several who did not get to the third one and still passed the exam.

16

SOE Skills You Need to Learn

Skills to master before your SOE Exam

PART OF PLAYING the game is mastering the skills you need to pass the Applied exam. These are a new set of skills, many of which you have not used before. You will need to learn and practice these skills well before you take the Applied exam.

Remember from chapter 14, when you start your Applied exam, you will be given a stem question and ten minutes to prepare for the oral part of the exam. During this preparation period, you will be left alone with the stem question written on the paper and a pen to write notes. Proper preparation of the stem before you meet the examiners will go a long way toward helping you pass the exam.

There are five main skills you should master before you take the Applied Exam.

Skill #1: Learn how to dissect the stem

The skill of dissecting the stem is one that should be practiced with every practice oral exam that you give or take. This skill allows you to thoroughly analyze the case and anticipate questions. You have time to organize your thoughts, build a road map, come up with plans and goals, and predict which complications and challenges may come your way. You should know that although you will likely be expecting certain complications they may throw a completely random one at you.

You are given the stem that has information on it about the case and empty space to make notes, build charts, and space to "think on the paper." You will want to make notes, but also leave a little space on the sheet, should you need to write down information they give you during the exam such as an arterial blood gas or other laboratory data provided by the examiners based on the case.

There are many different ways to dissect a stem. Below is one possible system. Feel free to mold it into your own system. The bottom line is you need some kind of system to keep your mind organized and productive, even when you are nervous.

Here are my twelve steps to dissect the stem.

1. Write the type of stem you have at the top of the page. (intraop/postop or preop/intraop)

- This will help you know which questions will be asked and will remind you which phase of care you are in.
- If you are doing the first session, which has the intraop/postop session, it does you no good to prep about preop work up or disagree with prep they obtained, because you are already in the OR.
- All your answers to the questions should be related to the phase of patient care you currently are in.

2. Actively read the case, asking yourself questions as you go along. Underline and put boxes around important information.
   - What is the age of the patient?
   - What is the weight of the patient?
   - What is the case?
   - Is this an elective, urgent, or emergency case?
     - This is critical for the preoperative case, because it determines how quickly you need to get to the operating room.
     - Expect the case might get upgraded.
   - What medications are the patient taking?
   - What are the vital signs? Are they normal?
   - Are you given labs?

3. Identify all of the patient's conditions and severity of those conditions, based on the information you are given.

- Underline the diagnosis and try to use context clues (lab or test data) to figure out the severity of the disease. Imagine what additional information you might need to assess this, if in preoperative section.
- This is the pitfall where some examinees try to make the patient sicker than they are.

4. Do a quick run through each organ system/issue to make sure everything is addressed. Not every system will be discussed every time in your stem, but it is good to have a system, so that things are not missed. I use the ABCs.

- A: airway
- B: breathing
- C: circulation
- D: endocrine
- E: electrolytes
- F: fluids
- G: gastrointestinal
- H: hematologic
- I: immune/infection risk
- J: joints/skin
- K: kidneys
- L: lines
- M: medications
- N: neuro
- O: operative location (location in the hospital) OR? Cath lab? Surgery center? Radiology?
- P: positioning

5. Identify each drug in the stem and its drug class.
   - This can help give you a clue about potential questions that might come your way.
6. Can you optimize anything?
   - before going to the OR (preop/intraop)
   - while in the OR (intraop/postop)
7. What is your plan for each problem in your system's review?
8. Are there conflicting plans? If so, attempt to prioritize.
   - Many times there are patient conditions that conflict with each other. For example, full stomach in a patient with increased intracranial pressure (ICP).
9. What are the common complications that could occur?
   - Complications are predictable—write them on your page, along with treatments to help you remember.
   - Examiners love to ask about comorbidities with multiorgan involvement. If your patient has obesity, hypertension, diabetes, or preeclampsia, make a brief list of anesthetic implications in your notes. Again, use the A, B, C, format.
   - What are your back up plans: bad airway on the stem? Write down a brief difficult airway algorithm.
10. Write down your ideal plan for premedication, induction, intubation, maintenance, and postoperative.

11. When you are done, go back and reread the stem, slowly.
    - Are there any other things you have missed?
12. Breathe.
    - When you get efficient, it's not unusual to finish the stem dissection with time to spare. Take a moment and relax.
    - If you still have time, write down some notes about ALS or PALS, or malignant hyperthermia so that you have them on your sheet.

These twelve steps should provide you with a road map, potential complications, and a good understanding of the case and the questions they will be asking about the case.

Skill #2: Learn how to predict questions and complications

We talked a little about this Skill #1.

There are only so many ways the Applied examiners can try and kill your patient. There will be no alien abductions, a land shark won't come thrashing through the OR doors, or any other plot lines from popular TV shows. After you do enough Applied exam practice, you will start to see themes and a limited number of questions that can be asked about the stem. Common problems are common.

This is where you are playing a mind game with the examiners. You can just blindly read the stem and take the questions as they are hurled at you, or you can anticipate what might be a question and write down some things on your paper before the question arrives.

This takes a little practice, which is why it is important to do as many practice exams as possible.

You have an OB stem—chances are you might have an epidural to troubleshoot. In this same stem, you might also have complications like the epidural not working, an epidural hematoma, a failed airway, uterine atony, a PALs resuscitation, HELLP syndrome, amniotic embolus, etc. You might also have an OB patient with heart disease or drug abuse issues that will create interesting conflicting goals.

All of your questions and complications will be related to the stem and the patient. When you are planning out your stem, you will be able to predict some of the complications that will be headed your way.

Just like when you were in medical school, you probably memorized the "most common list" for exams. This is also helpful for the Applied exam.

What is the most common cause of hypotension in a trauma? What is the most common cause of hypotension with a patient who is on an ACEI?

Do not try so hard to avoid these complications that you become inflexible or suggest plans different from your usual practice. The complications will happen if the examiners want it to happen. For example, do an awake fiber-optic on someone if it is indicated, but you cannot do it on everyone just to avoid talking about a failed airway. This is Mistake #5 that examinees make: Making the patient sicker than they are (chapter 18).

Similarly, it helps to have a memorized list of differentials for the usual offenders. For example: intraoperative hypotension, hypoxia, postoperative nausea/vomiting, etc.

Trying to predict the questions that will be asked is like building yourself a road map of where you may potentially be lead in the exam. You might not predict every question, but it might help you think through the most common categories to help you get to the other side.

Identify red flags in the stem that can help you predict the examiner's questions. For example, if a patient has coronary artery disease, your patient will likely have an intraoperative or postoperative MI, so be ready for it.

Skill #3: Learn how to answer the questions orally

This sounds kind of dumb, because you talk all the time, right? If you grew up in the United States, chances are you have taken all your exams on paper or on the computer. You have not taken many (if any) oral exams.

You have to practice this skill to get comfortable with it and it cannot be something that you practice "in your head." It needs to be done out loud and with other people. This is where taking and giving oral exams is helpful. The more you practice and get feedback, the better you will do.

1. You have to convince the examiners that you are a consultant physician, not a technician.
   - As stated above, don't use slang or jargon. Speak like a consultant.
2. State why you will do something—don't make the examiners ask you why.
   - The examiners will always want to know the reasoning behind your answer.
   - You have to let the examiners know you know the reasoning.
3. If you don't know the answer to one of their questions, state "**I don't know.**"
   - Don't try to pass off something as fact that you don't know.
4. Communicate to the examiners your plans and goals for each challenge that they ask you.
   - Don't talk yourself into a corner so that you have burned your bridges.
5. Don't be afraid of silence, the oral examiners will fill that space.
   - Don't ramble. You could end up talking about a topic that you don't know much and get into trouble.
6. Avoid topic you are weak in.
   - This goes along with rambling. You don't need to telegraph to the examiners that you are weak in a certain area, because they will drill down on it. Don't poke the bear.

Skill #4: How to manage grab-bag questions

When you get to the grab-bag questions, you are almost done with your SOE session.

After the main stem has been completed, you will move on to the grab-bag questions. These are the final three small clinical vignettes that are not related to the main stem or to each other.

It is vital that you not dwell on your stem questions. You have to move forward. What is done is done.

As long as you have kept on schedule, you should have ten minutes to finish these three quick cases. You finished the marathon of questions; now it is time to sprint to the end.

1. When you get to the grab-bag questions, you have to leave the main stem behind.
   - No matter how well you "feel" like you did, or how badly you feel like you did, you have to mentally "leave" the main stem behind and get on to the next set of questions.
2. When it is announced by your examiners that you are now moving on to the grab bag, turn your stem paper over and be prepared to start writing.
   - This is a physical act that tells you to leave the case behind, preps you to turn off the case, and get ready for the next one.
3. Each grab-bag question will be given to you orally, so you will have to focus on each one as it is given to you.

4. Write down the age of the patient, the type of surgery, and any lab values so that you can refer back to them.

5. Continue to answer the questions related to the patient in the current grab-bag questions.

6. When you finish the current grab-bag question and move on to the next, draw a line under your notes and be prepared to write down information for the grab-bag questions.

7. Again, leave the previous vignette behind and move on to the next.

8. You will have to sprint to get through these last three stems. Each vignette will be about 3.33 minutes, so you will have to be succinct.

9. Grab-bag questions commonly focus on subspecialty topics such as cardiac, OB, pain, or pediatrics. They will focus on quick management questions.

10. As stated previously, there will be times when you do not have time for all three grab-bag vignettes. This is OK and does not necessarily impact whether you pass or fail.

Skill #5: Be prepared to talk about your least favorite topics.

You will be covering a large amount of information on the exam. Be prepared for your least favorite topics to come back and haunt you. Know they are coming, so you don't panic when they do show up. Each grab-bag question is a relatively small part of the overall exam, so don't sweat it if you get a very difficult one.

Remember, each grab bag should last about 3.33 minutes. You can fend anything off for 3.33 minutes.

17

Achieve Key Targets for Your SOE

IN ORDER TO win the Applied game, you have to achieve several key targets. Some of these sound simple—and they are. But ignoring these targets may cause you to lose the game.

Key Target #1: Finish the SOE

I know this seems dumb, but it is not. Everyone finishes, right?

Wrong.

Unlike written exams, where you know exactly how many questions you have left, you won't know how much of the exam you have left or how much more time you have to take the exam.

You have thirty-five minutes to get through the main stem, plus three grab-bag questions. You know the exam is thirty-five minutes in length, but when you are taking the exam, you don't know exactly where you are in the exam.

You need to do your best to through all three grab bags. It is the examiner's job to control your pace, but if you can tell they are trying to speed you up, it is for good reason. they are trying to help you.

Although you are taking the exam, you are also affecting the flow and speed of the exam.

If you don't make it to the grab-bag questions, then you lose out on possible points toward a passing score.

There are some examinees who don't complete all the grab bags, and yet they pass. You will have to amass as many points as you can to pass. Your goal should be to get through all the grab bags, but if it doesn't happen, don't freak out.

There are four things you can do to help get yourself through the SOE.

1. Answer the question directly and efficiently. Being overly verbose will take time. Get to the point. If the examiners have to ask you why you do something each time, that takes time as well. Let's look in on Dr. Larry G. Scope, our crash test dummy for the exam.

   "Dr. Scope, would you use a Rapid Sequence Induction on this patient?"

   "Yes, I would—"

   (Awkward pause.)

"Why?" asks the annoyed oral board examiner.

"Because the patient has a full stomach."

"Why do you think the patient has a full stomach?"

"Because the patient had a recent meal and de-layed gastric emptying."

"Why do you think the patient has delayed gas-tric emptying?"

"Progesterone decreases gastric emptying."

Holy Smokes! As painful as that was to read, try be-ing the examiner and sitting through that exchange.

Try it this way:

"Dr. Scope, would you use a Rapid Sequence Induction on this patient?"

"Yes, I would choose a rapid sequence induction because this pregnant patient is considered a full stomach. She had a recent meal and delayed gastric emptying, which is known to be caused by increased progesterone level."

Which one is better?[7]

2. Use "buzz words" every chance you can. The exam-iners may be zoning out during your exam, so make sure they hear the words they are looking for, so you can move on. Give them every opportunity to move you forward in the exam.

---

7 Random thought. If you have progesterone as a choice, and you don't know the answer, it is usually progesterone—unless it is not.

3. If you don't know the answer, instead of trying to figure it out (and getting barraged with questions in the meantime), state "I don't know" or "the name escapes me at this time."

    If you don't know the answer, don't guess. Reasonable guesses are fine, but "shot in the dark" answers will get you into trouble. When you do a shot in the dark, then the examiners will believe that you think it is the right answer and you go down a rabbit hole full of pain.

    "Dr. Scope, are succinylcholine and cisatracurium eliminated by the same mechanism."

    Hmm...I don't know. "Yes they are."

    "So if a patient has a family history of malignant hyperthermia, then is cisatracurium also contraindicated."

    Oh snap. I guess it is right...why else would they ask it? But I thought that sux was the only contraindicated muscle relaxant. Hesitantly, "Yes, that is correct. Both are eliminated by the pseudocholinesterase."

    "What is the mechanism of the malignant hyperthermia?"

    "The ryanodine receptor."

    "So the ryanodine receptor is responsible for the elimination process?"

    "I guess so."

    WRONG.

    You get the right idea.

4. Answer every question, as though it is related to the patient in the stem. Don't try to answer the question broadly, answer for the patient in front of you. If you answer broadly, then the examiners will ask you to narrow it down, which **causes you to answer the same question a second time**. BOOOO!

Key Target #2: Don't get lost

You have to keep your mental bearings as you move through the exam. If you forget where you are in the sequence of the case (preop/intraop/postop) or you forget about the patient in front of you, you may get hosed.

1. For your major stem, remember if you are doing the intraop/postop or preop/intraop stem. (That's why I have you write it on your stem so you don't forget.) The first stem you are given is long, because all the preop work has been done and you are in the OR. There is no going back to preop, because you are already in the OR. Likewise, on the second stem, don't go to the OR until the patient is optimized. "Optimized" does not equal "healthy"; it means that the patient is as good as they are going to get. Even if the work up is not done, you might be forced into the OR with the case changing from urgent to emergency. You better go. I would not put it past the oral examiners to turn it into a hostage situation and force

you into the room at gun point if you will not go on your own accord. (Or not go, which means you get to come back next year and do it all again.)

2. Dissect the stem systematically, then take a moment to tie in the patient history, the patient conditions and all the bad stuff that can go wrong. While ten minutes does not seem like a long time, it is plenty of time to do a proper dissection. As you get more practice, you will be able to dissect the stem faster and more efficiently. When you get good, you will have extra time on your hands to predict questions and complications (see chapter 16).

3. Every question is related to the patient in the stem, unless otherwise stated by the examiners. Some examinees forget to relate the questions back to the patient who is in front of them.

4. Do not make the patient sicker than they are. If you assume a bad airway and start going down that path, then not only do you waste time, you may miss out on getting to questions you may know very well later in the case. (Remember Key Target #1: Finish the exam.) It is safe to assume. "Assuming the airway exam is reassuring…" or "Assuming his cardiac disease is optimized…"

Key Target #3: Stay cool when brought down the "wrong path"

We talked about this briefly under the expectations section, but it is worth restating. This is where you are given the choice between two things and asked why/why not you would choose something. It can be a drug, a technique, a device, whatever. You will give your reason why you would do something, and the Board Examiners will bring you down another road.

Why?

One of the following two things are happening:

1. The examiner is trying to figure out your adaptability or
2. The questions in front of her wants to push you down that path.

Either way, you will be going down the path you don't want to go—you have to flow with it.

If they want to take you down the path, they will take you down the path. Arguing about it won't help.

Let's look in on Dr. Scope:

-   "Dr. Scope, would you choose a general or regional anesthetic?"
-   "I would choose a general anesthetic in this patient because (1) *reason*, (2) *great reason*, and (3) *fantastic reason*."
-   "Let's say you decide to do a regional technique instead, which one would you choose?"
-   "I wouldn't do a regional technique" *nincompoop* "because of (1) *reason*, (2) *OK reason*, and (3) *crummy reason*."

- "Your partner started the case as a regional, became ill, and you had to take it over."
- "I would refuse to take the case over."
- "Dr. Scope, a deranged patient breaks into the Ready Room, puts a gun to your head and tells you to take over the case or you die. You cannot run, hide, or fight. If he kills you, you fail this exam."
- "Under the circumstances, I think a regional technique would be an excellent choice" *spoken through a clenched smile.*

OK, that was a little drastic, but you get the point.

Stalling only delays the inevitable and burns time, which also (you guessed it) violates Key Target #1.

When you are brought down the road, think of the time when your faculty wanted to do some crazy technique and you didn't have a choice. Stay cool when you are brought down a path you don't want to go. In fact, expect to be brought down a bad path and you will not be surprised by the ordeal.

These key targets will help you stay on the path to success. In the next chapter, we will talk about the top seven mistakes that Applied examinees make and how you can avoid them.

18

Top Seven Applied Examinee Mistakes

THERE ARE MANY mistakes that can be made during an Applied exam. Much like complications are predictable, these top seven Applied examinee mistakes are made routinely and they telegraph to your Applied examiner that you are not prepared for the exam. Avoid these top seven mistakes and you are headed toward a successful test.

Mistake #1: Repeating the question
You have been trained at some point in your schooling to repeat the question that was asked. This buys you some time and it makes sure you heard the question answer correctly.

Don't do it.

For the love of Sevoflurane, get out of the habit of repeating the question. It burns time, annoys the examiners, and you lose style points.

Don't be afraid of silence. Being silent for a moment or two will be better tolerated by the examiner than repeating the question.

Mistake #2: Not answering the question

This sounds silly, but it happens all the time. You are asked a question, and you feel the need to explain all the things that it is not, before stating what it is. You feel the need to set up the question before answering it. Instead, answer the questions directly and immediately state why you would do it.[8] "What?" you say.

Here is what it looks like:

The examiner holds up a writing pen.

"What is this, Dr. Scope?"

"I know that it is an instrument usually used for writing on paper, but it can be used to write on walls in a pinch. It is not a crayon, because it is not made of wax. It is not a pencil, because it doesn't have graphite. It is not a marker, because it can't be used on a white board very well. So it must be a pen."

---

8 If you really want to see a horrible way to not answer a question, Google "The Battle of Wits with Vizzini" from *The Princess Bride*—it is brilliant. In fact, go right now and watch this four-minute scene. You need a break, and a good laugh. Then come back.

Arrggggg.

You will probably get stabbed with that very pen if you answer like that.

This wouldn't happen you say?

Here is what it looks like in the exam:

The examiner asks, "Which paralytic would you use in this patient?"

"I know that I would not use succinylcholine because the patient has a CVA with left-sided paralysis, which might lead to release of potassium due to extrajunctional receptors and potentially cardiac arrhythmias. I also would not use rocuronium, because she has decreased renal function, and I would not use pancuronium, because I would be worried about the ensuing tachycardia. I would use cisatracurium."

Again, painful.

Answer the question and move on.

Mistake #3: Not answering the question with the current patient in mind

Every question asked within the exam is **related to the patient in the stem**. When you get to the grab-bag questions, every question that follows those short stems relates only to the grab-bag question.

Not every patient. Not a patient with a bad airway, nor a pediatric patient if your stem is OB, nor a cardiac patient coming off bypass.

If the question comes within the main stem, or in the grab bag, the question only relates to the patient within the stem. Narrow down your answers to your differential based only on the patient in front of you.

Always think of every question as related to the stem patient, unless the examiner states otherwise.

Mistake #4: Not being concerned

Unlike in real life (when you are trying to calm patients and surgeons) you are always concerned during the Applied exam.

ALWAYS.

The oral boards are testing to see if you can safely take care of patients.

"Dr. Scope, are you concerned about the patient's low hemoglobin?"

"No. I am sure that the surgeon will not lose much blood (he told me so), and I am sure that I can get blood if need be."

WRONG.

"Dr. Scope, are you concerned about the patient's low hemoglobin?"

"Yes, I am concerned because there is the possibility of losing blood in this surgery; the patient has coronary artery disease, and because of past transfusions, he might be a challenge to type and cross quickly."

You get the point. You are always concerned. All The Time.

Mistake #5: Making the patient any sicker than they are

Approach every patient like they are the sickest patient in the world. You go into the OR to do a Lap Chole and you are calling for the difficult airway cart to do an awake fiber-optic, (even though there is no reason to believe the patient has a bad airway,) you are planning to "line up" the patient with a Swan Ganz, an A-line, a foley, and you have the massive transfusion protocol activated before you get into the OR.

Now, the scenario might change and the patient might become sicker, but unless stated in the stem or by the examiners, the patient is as healthy as stated.

You can always hedge your bets and state "Assuming..."

"How would you induce this patient, Dr. Scope?"

"**Assuming** the patient has a normal looking airway, I would proceed with a rapid sequence induction because of the patient's full stomach."

"Assuming" allows you to let the examiners know that you are basing your decision on the patient in the stem and the current information you have in hand. The examiners have the patient in the stem in mind, so you should as well. If you start chasing down complications that are not there, you are violating Key Target #1, because you are burning time.

Mistake #6: Saying "I could" instead of "I would"

You **could** do a lot of things...but what **would** you do?

By stating "I could..." you are not making a decision, you are making a list of possibilities. I could start an arterial line, place a central line, and float in a pulmonary artery catheter on every single anesthesia case I do—but would I? No and neither would you.

It is a subtle wording choice, but it doesn't really answer the question, which violates Mistake #2. The examiners are aware that you know of all the things **you could do**, but they are more interested i**n what would you do.**

You have to make a commitment to your answer.

Mistake #7: Getting angry during the exam

With the amount of stress you are under and the sheer numbers of questions you are going to be asked, it is a prime time to get pissed off. This doesn't happen very often, but it can happen. When you get angry on top of being nervous, it can be a disastrous combination. After reading through the Expectations section (chapter 12), you should be well aware of the things that would make you upset.

Keep calm, keep your head in the game, and keep moving the exam forward. They have only thirty-five minutes to torment you, then it will end.

Mistake #7: Not examining the patient

If you don't specifically state that you would examine the patient, the examiners may not assume that you are examining your patient. How would you examine your patient?

What are you listening for?

Would you listen for breath sounds? Absent breath sounds?

Are you listening for wheeze, or heart murmur? Where would you listen?

If you don't state it, then the examiners don't know that you are thinking about it.

Mistake #8: Being cavalier, overly conservative, or suggesting techniques you don't use or understand

You want to present a very textbook answer to the questions that are being asked. You want to stick to a very conservative version of your normal practice. We all learned anesthesia hacks during our training. You might have even gotten away with a shortcut or two. When you are taking the Applied exam, you want to present an appropriate amount of conservatism.

Likewise, you don't want to be so conservative that you come across as inflexible or unrealistic. It will annoy the examiners if you suggest ultraconservative or unrealistic plans that don't work in the "real world."

Avoid using techniques that you have not used during your training. You will not have a good working knowledge of them and could very well bring about a set of complications that you will not be able to handle.

19

Tactics to Help you Communicate with the Applied Examiners

THERE ARE A handful of phrases you should have at the tip of your tongue. These will help you better communicate with the examiners and show that you are working to answer the question and are not stalling. It also helps to convey a level of decorum in line with the spirit of the Applied exam. Be careful not to come off as sounding overprepared. I know, it sounds counterintuitive, but you don't want to seem "too prepared" or "too polished," because you will come across as being arrogant.

Phrase #1: "I don't recall at this time" or "I would have to look that up"

This is an alternate to the phrase, "I don't know." It conveys two things: (1) You **do** know it, but you **can't** remember it at this time, and (2) You are not wasting time trying to come up with the answer.

This also takes some stress off you and mentally tells yourself that you know this thing, just not right now.

Phrase #2: "The name escapes me at this time"

This is similar to phrase number one. This one is used when you are asked a specific diagnosis. You may be able to describe everything about it, but you can't name it.

Again, this will take some mental pressure off you and keep you from completely freaking out.

Phrase #3: "It depends"

The Applied exam has many areas that are not black and white. You will be tested in the areas of gray, because that is where you will live in your career as an anesthesiologist.

By stating "It depends" you are conveying to the examiners that you realize the issue is not black and white (and keeps you from painting yourself into a corner by stating something that is dependent on the patient and the circumstances). There are very few absolutes in life and this includes the scenarios in the Applied exam.

"Dr. Scope, would use regional anesthesia in this patient?"

"I would not, because of reason A, reason B, and really good reason C."

"Would you ever use regional anesthesia is a situation like this?"

"It depends. If I didn't need to provide muscle relaxation for the surgeon, and the patient was not on current anticoagulant, then yes, I would consider regional anesthesia."

This phrase allows you to show flexibility and a breadth of knowledge.

Phrase #4: "Assuming…"

This is a great phase to assert the healthiness of the patient. It shows that you are thinking about the patient in front of you.

"Assuming the patient has a normal airway evaluation, I would…"

"Assuming the echocardiogram shows good ventricular function and appropriate ejection fraction, I would…"

Now, this also relates to not making the patient sicker than they are. (chapter 17 - Key Target #2). The examiners may ask you something like, "What if the echocardiogram shows poor filling and wall motion abnormalities?" They just made the patient sicker, and you can adjust as necessary.

Phrase to AVOID
"I would go to the bedside"

This is a phrase that is commonly used at a popular Applied exam review course, and it tends to get overused. I have no problem with you taking a review course, and I believe that it is a personal decision (see chapter 26). There may be some Applied examiners who feel otherwise. This goes along with not looking too polished, and you want to seem prepared, but not like you "cheated" by taking a review course.

By all means, please perform a physical exam (see Mistake #7) when it is appropriate, but use your own phrasing.

Phrases with medical jargon

This is not a time to have an anesthesia lounge discussion. Instead of saying "I would sleep the patient with some pro-pofol," say "I would provide a smooth IV induction utilizing propofol." Instead of "I would give him some gas," say "I would increase the volatile anesthetic to deepen the anesthesia." (You sound smarter already.)

20

Tactics to Help you Hack
Your Applied Exam

BELOW YOU WILL find three hacks to help you prepare for the Applied exam. Most of these hacks and phrases have been talked about throughout this book, but I felt like it was fitting to put them all in one place for a quick review.

Hack #1: Finish the exam

We have already talked about this one in other sections of the book, but it is worth restating the obvious. Your goal should be to get through the whole exam so that you get as many points as possible. Because the grab bags are on different topics than the main stem questions, you might be able to rack up some points at the very end of the exam. If you do not get to those questions, you are leaving possible points on the table. Every point that you are able to obtain gets you closer to a passing score. If you don't finish your stem plus the three grab-bag questions, it will be harder to pass the exam. Not impossible, just harder.

Hack #2: Mentally go to the OR

When you are answering questions about what you would do in certain clinical situations, it helps to "be in the same environment" to help you trigger memories. To help you think through problems, imagine yourself in your home OR as you take the exam. Mentally going to the OR where you take care of those types of patient helps you get your head is in the right place.

You know the layout of your home institution like the back of your hand. Neurosurgery is done in ORs #11 and #12, ortho in #15, emergency general surgery in OR #7. You get the idea.

Because all questions are related to the stem, when you go to the OR, you narrow down the possibilities of the things that can go wrong. Much like you won't be doing open-heart surgery in OB suite (unless it is a really bad day), going to the OR helps you to mentally frame your answers.

When you have an OB case, go the OB floor in your mind and enter the room. Mentally "look" around where you set up your drugs, where your suction is, and how you set up the room. This will help you trigger memories and help you with the Applied exam.

Hack #3: Mentally walk the examiners into your OR

Since you are already imagining yourself in the OR, bring the examiners with you. Talk them through exactly what you would do. Tell them exactly what you are going to do, step by step. Because they don't know you, you have to tell them everything. When you examine the patient, tell them how as we discussed in the last chapter.

For example: "What would you do if the patient starts bucking on the tube?"

"I would switch the ventilator to manual and feel the compliance of the bag. Assuming that the vital signs are stable, I would then deepen the anesthesia plane with propofol and fentanyl." (Did you see that "assuming"? It is your friend.)

Tell them exactly what you would do.

Hack #4: Be comfortable with being uncomfortable

The Applied exam will be one of the most stressful exams you will take during your road to anesthesiology board certification. You will be asked a boatload of questions in a short period of time, many of which you will know, some of which you may not know.

There will be times of self-doubt as you are brought down a road in which you do not want to go. This will be a very uncomfortable feeling.

Even in this uncomfortable situation, try to stay as re-laxed as possible. Anticipate being uncomfortable, not so that you get tense, but so that you will know what to expect.

You just have thirty-five minutes with your captors—examiners—then you are either off to the next room for the OSCE, or off to the airport to get out of there.

Realize it, acknowledge it, and move on. You've got an exam to ace.

21

High-yield Final Review Information

A s you get closer to the Applied exam, you will naturally start tapering your studying. This is not an exam that you can cram for. There are, however, some high-yield topics that would be good to do a brief review on, the day or two before your exam. This quick review will help you when the stress of the looming exam is coming down on you. This is not an all-inclusive list, but one that should hit some high points for you.

High-yield areas to be reviewed

Basic Anesthesia Stuff

- ASA Physical Status
  - I know you have used these for the last three years, but review the exact definition, so that you have it firmly in your mind.
- The Standard ASA Monitors
  - This comes up more than you would think.
  - Pulse Oximetry, Noninvasive BP, ECG, temperature, $EtCO_2$, Inspiratory Oxygen Monitor
    - Think of these as four on the patient and two on the machine to remember these.
- ACLS
  - Know your first-line drugs and maneuvers.
  - You might be coding a patient during the exam.
- PALS
  - Know your first-line drugs and how they differ from adults.
- New York Heart Association Functional Classification
  - How to do further work up
- Malignant Hyperthermia (MH)
  - Signs/symptoms/diagnosis/treatment
  - Of all the complications that can happen during anesthesia, MH is the one thing every anesthesiologist is considered an expert in.
  - Be sure to keep this in your differential when it is appropriate.

Common problems

- Hypoxia differential
- Hypotension differential
- Hypercarbia differential

Laboratory stuff

- ABG
  - Acidosis, alkalosis, respiratory, metabolic, and mixed
- ACT values
  - Know the appropriate values needed for cardiac bypass.
- PT, PTT, INR
  - Good for regional stuff
- Allowable blood loss

Cardiac stems

- Standard bypass case
- Pacemaker designations
  - DDD, DDO, and so on

OB Stems

- STAT C-section
  - A one-sided block
- The failed airway
- HELLP syndrome

Neuro stems

- STAT crani for trauma
  - CT for trauma
  - Aneurysm clipping

Pediatric stems

- TEF types, including most common
- Pyloric stenosis
- Diaphragmatic hernia
- Omphalocele versus Gastroschisis
- APGAR score
  - Dr. Apgar was an anesthesiologist—know your scoring

Final Preparations for the Applied Exam

You will want to finish off the third and final step of board certification as soon as you can adequately prepare yourself. This allows you to tap into your anesthesia knowledge to help you pass the Applied exam. You may also need to complete the Applied exam so that you can sit for another board.

For example, you have to successfully pass the Applied exam before you are able to sit for pediatric anesthesiology board certification, which is given in the fall.

Critical care boards are the same way as well You can't even register until you have the passing score in hand, which is very important to know because it is only offered once a year in August. If you miss the May deadline for the Applied exam, you will have to wait a whole year, which can cost you a large chunk of your salary.

Not only do you want to finish off your board certification to complete it, your salary (or more likely an increase in your salary) may depend on your board certification.

This could mean hundreds of thousands of dollars.

You will want to take the Applied exam soon after the Advanced exam, but balance it with your ability to properly prepare for it with your work schedule. Don't rush through this process just to get it over with. If you fail the Applied exam, because you didn't properly prepare, you will have to wait a full year to take it again.

The Applied exam is now scheduled to be given over multiple months. (In the past, it was given in April and October only.) Now, because of the wide range, choosing when to take it can be a little daunting.

Look at your work schedule (or your rotation schedule) to come up with the best time to sit for the Applied exam. You may choose to take it earlier in the cycle, as opposed to later. You will also want to keep in mind your local weather while planning your exam date, because you don't want to miss your flight because of weather conditions (see chapter 22).

Don't try to study for the Applied exam at the same time as another specialty board exam.

Bad idea.

Three things to keep in mind for the Applied Exam

There are three things to keep in mind when gearing up for the Applied exam. You are going to need to do the following:

1. Review your anesthesia knowledge so that it stays fresh in your mind.
2. Practice your Applied exam skills such as dissecting stem questions and practicing answering oral questions. (Plan to take twenty-five to thirty-five practice exams with a study partner or Applied examiner.)
3. Schedule the date of your Applied exam based on your work schedule and give yourself enough time to adequately prepare. Consider taking some additional vacation days around the time of your exam to help you rest up before the exam.

22

Travel Guide for the Applied Exam

A FTER ALL THE preparation you invest in getting ready for the Applied exam, there is one more hurdle to overcome—the travel involved with taking the exam.

You will have more stress than you can predict. By minimizing as much extraneous stress as possible, you will reduce your overall stress for the exam. Some of the recommendations will cost you a little money, but they are well worth the price to control as much of the testing experience as possible.

When you decrease the number of variables that you will encounter during travel, it means fewer things can go wrong. Much of the information here has been gleaned from people who have taken the Applied exam in the last few years.

Before you leave

Plan out your travel as much early as possible. There are a few things you can do, even before you leave, to make the experience less painful.

1. Learn about flying in and out of Raleigh-Durham Airport

The new Applied exam will be given at the ABA testing center in North Carolina. Because it will be given in the same location for everyone, there will be a certain amount of uniformity in what the testing environment you will encounter will be like. This is good because it decreases the number of variables that you will encounter.

For most examinees, you will be flying in to Raleigh-Durham International Airport. The Raleigh-Durham International Airport (Airport Code: RDU) is located northeast of Raleigh and is a small airport with two terminals. Each terminal has multiple restaurant choices (Terminal two has many more choices than Terminal one), and each has a Starbucks® Coffee Shop.

2. Plan your flight with the weather in mind

When you sign up for the exam, keep in mind your local weather when planning the trip. If you come from an area that tends to have relatively late winter storms or seasonal hurricanes, then you might want to schedule your exam closer to summer. You don't want an ice storm to cancel your flight.

3. Plan when you want to fly into RDU

Plan to fly into Raleigh-Durham at least early in the day before the exam. The best advice I got was to fly in two days before the exam.[9] The reason for this is twofold:

1. You rarely sleep well the first night in a hotel room. It's a new environment with new sounds and feel.
2. If you have a flight delay, you have a little more time to make it to a hotel, should you need to change flights.

4. Plan your flight out

When you book your flight out of Raleigh, make sure you leave enough time to finish the exam and take the shuttle to get back to the airport. You will have your exam schedule, so you will know when your exam day will end.

Plan at least a two-hour buffer between when your exam finishes and your flight takes off. To be on the safe side, plan for third hours. You don't want to be stressing about missing your flight when you are taking the exam. Plus, because you

---

9 If you have your exam on a Monday, then you would want to fly in on Saturday. It is a little harder to fly in two days early, but the extra cost would be well worth it.

know the airport, you can get to the airport and find some-place to hang out for some time.

5. Fly carry-on only

When you do fly in, consider flying carry-on only. This is a huge travel hack that will save you the stress of potentially lost luggage. (I know a faculty member who had his luggage lost during his oral exam—he almost had to take the exam in sweatpants or buy a suit on a Sunday night.)

Also, if your flight gets cancelled due to mechanical is-sues, bad weather, and so on, you have your luggage with you. You can choose to get on another flight at the last minute—either coming or going from Raleigh-Durham. Every good anesthesiologist has a backup plan—your flight to the Applied exam should be no different.

If you cannot bring yourself to fly carry-on only, at least have your clothes of the exam day and toiletries with you. I have become a carry-on freak, so I have even put together an article on how to fly carry-on only for you at AnesthesiaMadeEasy.com/carryon.

6. Plan your hotel accommodations

The ABA has contracted with a hotel in Raleigh (Hilton North Raleigh/Midtown) to be the registration site for the Applied exams. Even if you live in the area, you will be picked up at the Hilton and brought to the testing center. (This is the hotel that has been used in the past, but you will be told specifically which hotel they will use in your acceptance e-mail.) Everyone must register for the exam at the designated hotel before boarding the shuttle to the ABA Assessment Center (see chapter 23).

I would recommend staying at the hotel the night before. It decreases the number of things that can go wrong on the day of the exam. The last thing you need is to have your car break down, over sleep, or have bad weather that prevents you from making it to the hotel in time.

Examiners stay in a different hotel right next to the ABA offices in order to minimize changes that examiners and examinees cross paths prior to the exam.

7. Learn what to expect at the ABA Assessment Center

Go to our website (AnesthesiaMadeEasy.com/travel) to see videos from the ABA about what the Applied Exam looks like.

Seriously.

Knowing what the environment will be like will help take out some of the surprises from the day. When you take the exam, you will be seated in a glassed-in room, with the examiners looking at iPads. You will see them read as you move along.

One examiner thought they were filming her with the iPad and it threw her off. The camera is in the corner, not on the iPad.

Your travel day

The big day has come, and have decided to fly into Raleigh-Durham International Airport two days early. You glide past the luggage claim, because you have packed carry-on only, and head out to get a taxi cab. During the thirty-minute ride to the hotel, you are relaxed, because you have everything you need with you.

Your time in the hotel

The day before the exam, plan on sequestering yourself in your room. This is where you go on a lock down. Don't go to the restaurant, don't go to the lobby, don't meet up with friends. This is your time to stay away from others and the intense amount of stress they can bring with them. (Unless it's a welcome distraction and your friends are not taking the exam.)

Avoid other exam takers at all costs. This is a stressful exam and nothing breeds fear like seeing other people freaking out.

While you are sequestered, order room service, watch trash TV, or a good documentary, and lay low.

Also, this is not the time to be adventurous with the food you eat. Don't try something that could potentially cause you to get sick.

Hotel sleeping hacks

It can be a challenge to sleep well when you travel, especially when you are traveling for an exam. You are in a strange place, with strange sounds (and sometimes smells), you might be going through a different time zone, you have been traveling, and you have a hectic schedule. Using the techniques below will help you maximize your sleep and help you wake up refreshed.

Use sleep hygiene

Think back to your medical school days when you learned about sleep hygiene. Put it to use now to get the best sleep that you can as you get ready for the Applied exam. You will want to optimize your environment and yourself.

Build your travel cocoon

Start with the environment of your hotel room. You will want to build your cocoon to hopefully provide a great place to rest and sleep.

Temperature: Turn down the temperature in the room and set the AC or Heat Fan from "auto" to "on." By keeping the fan running on the unit, this will provide a constant white noise, and you won't be woken up with the AC or heat turning on and off.

Light: Unplug the alarm clock in the room and blacken the room. If there is light coming from the hallway under the door, use a towel to block it out. Consider bringing a sleep mask to help block out the light as well. You want a completely darkened environment.

Activity: Don't turn on the TV and watch in bed. If you watch TV, then do it in a chair. You want to prep your bed for sleeping. And don't study in bed either.

Sound: Ask for a room away from the elevator and meeting rooms and considering using ear plugs.[10] Setting the AC/heat blower to "on" will also produce white noise to help you sleep. Consider getting a white noise machine for travel.

Interruptions: Set your phone to "Do Not Disturb" because you are bound to get a phone call or text from someone.

Setting: You want your setting to have the least amount of stress producing elements, so declutter and neaten up the room before you go to bed. Lay out and iron your clothes for the next day. Pack up everything that you won't be using to declutter the hotel room.

Optimize yourself

As above, you want to make your night-time routine as close to your normal as possible.

Nighttime diet: Eat a meal with some fat and protein three hours before going to sleep to help prime

---

10 As long as you can still hear your alarm clock.

yourself. Limit your caffeine and alcohol consumption the day before your Applied exam.

Shut down your brain: Dim the lights in your room and avoid the TV and computer screens; don't read on your tablet in bed. If you want to read, then use a device that uses indirect light such as Kindle. Consider reading fiction to allow yourself to sleep. If you want to do some last-minute studying, do it several hours before going to bed.

This is not the time to try medical sleep aids for the first time. The last thing you need is to have a hangover affect the next day and mess up your exam.

23

The Day You Take the Exam

*At a cardiac arrest, the first procedure is to
take your own pulse.*

—RULE NUMBER 3 IN *HOUSE OF GOD*

YOU ARE WELL rested because you flew into RDU two
days early, had a day to rest and glance over a few review
topics and got a good night's sleep.

Now the big day has arrived and you are about to put all
your preparation to the test. This quick guide should allevi-
ate some stress and help you mentally prepare for what is to
come.

When you wake up

Make sure you have multiple alarms set on your phone to help you wake up and consider having a wake-up call scheduled from the front desk of the hotel.

Eat a good breakfast, pack up your bag, and get dressed for the exam.

1. Dress like it is a professional job interview.
    *   Wear a dark, conservative suit. This is not the time to "be cute" or "fashionable." You have a name tag on, other than that, you want to blend in.
    *   Men, wear a tie.
    *   Women, if you are more comfortable in a pantsuit, or dress suit, it doesn't matter. You will do better in whichever one is more comfortable to you.
    *   **Do not wear a white coat.** You will stick out like a medical school student on a rotation.

Get ready to leave for the ABA Assessment Center

Pack up your bag. You have two options:

1. Have it stored at the hotel behind the bellhop station or
2. Bring it with you on the shuttle (which I think is the better alternative)

Either way, make sure that you have your needed paperwork and ID to present for registration for the Applied exam.

Sign in with the ABA representatives at the hotel and shuttle ride to the ABA Testing Center

Even if you are not staying at the designated hotel for the exam, you still must be picked up at the hotel to get to the testing center. You will be registered at the Hotel, then piled into a van with other examinees and brought to the testing center.

You will register and be picked up in the lobby of the official ABA hotel and taken to the ABA Assessment Center in a shuttle bus. Once you register, you will be given a name tag and asked to wait for the shuttle bus. Expect to have nineteen other people there with you.

You might have to wait thirty minutes until the shuttle shows up, so be prepared for this. You will be nervous, so will everyone else.

Arriving at the ABA Assessment Center

When you arrive at the ABA Assessment Center, plan for two scenarios:

1) You will have to leave everything on the bus. Everything. You will then leave the bus and enter the ABA testing center.

2) You can bring in a small number of personal items, which will be left in a small, square locker.

Either way, you should have nothing with you. No cell phone, no purse, no bag, no nothing. I know one test taker that had to remove a hair clip from her head and leave it on the bus as well.[11]

You will file into a room with two rows of ten chairs each. You will then be shown an orientation video. You are not allowed to ask questions, because by this point in the process, you should know what to expect. Be glad they don't allow examinees to ask questions.[12]

The orientation video should be telling you things you already know sense you have prepared by looking at the videos on the ABA website. After the orientation video, you will be given your first stem and given exactly ten minutes to prep for your first round of questions.

You are well prepared for the Applied exam, so have a go at it.

---

11 I had one former fellow call another one during the exam, thinking that it would be over by the time he called. The fellow taking the exam had brought her phone with her, and it was ringing during the exam. She was very lucky that the examiners let it slide. It could have been seen as an exam violation, and she could have been failed. For the love of Sevoflurane, leave your cell phone and don't bring it with you.

12 At my orientation, one of my fellow examinees asked "Do the examiners know how many times I have taken the oral exam." If you think the room was tense then, it got a whole lot more stressful.

Expect what the Applied Exam day will be like

You will either be in the group that starts with the SOE or the OSCE. Review the proposed schedule at our website at AnesthesiaMadeEasy.com/OSCE.

This schedule may change, so check back at the website to as you get closer to your exam to help you prepare for the schedule of the day.

When your exam is complete

Once you are done with your exam, you will want to get out of there as quickly as possible, no matter how well things went. When all the testing is complete, you will then re-board the ABA shuttle and will be driven back to the hotel.

If you don't need to be dropped off at the hotel, they will continue on to the airport. (So bring your luggage with you to get a free ride to the airport and get out of there quicker.) The last thing you will want to do is go back to the hotel, pack up your bag, check out (you are probably going to be too late for that), and get a shuttle to the airport. You will want to streamline your egress from Raleigh-Durham every step of the way.

Once you get to the airport, you can have some down-time and relax. Go find an establishment of your choice, get a beverage of your choice, and make sure you know from which gate your plane is leaving.

The post Applied Exams blues

No matter how well your Applied exam went, you will feel like you failed. There will be some of your fellow residents who will text how they "just know" they failed the exam, but no one really knows. Some will be more dramatic than others, but regardless to say, you will probably not walk out of the Assessment Center high flying and fist bumping your flight crew on the way out.

Realize that you will start to replay the exam on the way home. You will think of all the stuff you got wrong. Most people think they failed—most are wrong. Most people pass. Recognize that even if you gave a different answer than another examinee, it doesn't mean you both can't pass.

The exam is behind you, enjoy the flight home, and toast me midair when you are halfway home.

I'll be toasting you right back.

Strong work.

Get some rest, my friend.

24

Luck

Luck is what happens when preparation meets opportunity.

— SENECA THE YOUNGER

YOU THOUGHT I would leave out luck?

No way.

As with any game, there will be a certain amount of luck to passing the Basic and Advanced exams, getting through residency, and getting board certified.

I have known residents whose children were delivered the night before the written exam. I know residents/fellows who were eight months pregnant during the Applied exam. You may have a bad call schedule, a busy week, or an unexpected illness.

Sometimes luck will be on your side, and other times, it will not. The better you prepare, the less you will have to rely on luck to get you through.

Sometimes a pediatric fellow gets a pediatric stem and sometimes they get a cardiac stem.

You can't pick your questions on the exam, and you can't pick your Applied exam examiners. But by building your anesthesiology knowledge base, preparing for the exams, tracking to make sure you graduate from residency, and honing your skills for the exam, you are well on your way to becoming board certified.

As I have mentioned earlier, too many residents rely on knowledge and luck to get them through the anesthesiology board process.

Don't rely on luck, because it is unpredictable.

Prepare the best that you can, before the exams. Don't wait till the last moment to study, and don't hope for an easy exam. That is not a good strategy. You will be given the opportunity to take these three exams to become board certified. With adequate preparation, you will pass all of the exams, no matter what life throws at you.

Section Five

Year-by-Year Checklists

WE HAVE COVERED heaps of information in this book so far. How do you put it all together and actually use the information in this book?

Below you will find how to use the information for each part of your training.

I have also included links to resources on our website to help you work toward your board certification in anesthesiology.

25

Checklist for Your CB Year (Intern Year)

General information

Y OU WILL LEARN more during your CB year that you will use later in your career and training than you know. It is during your CB year that you are learning to become a physician, not just a technician.

You will have anywhere from zero to six months of anesthesiology rotations during this time.[13] In most programs, you will be spending between zero and two months in anesthesiology during your CB year.

---

13 Those programs that have six months of anesthesia during the CB year have a combined two-year schedule. This is where the CB and CA-1 year is blended so that you do 6 months of anesthesiology rotations during your CB year and six months of anesthesiology rotations during your CA-1 year, or any variety of combinations.

Since a majority of your time will be spent doing rotations other than anesthesiology, you will have to be studying for those other disciplines as well. It is a huge challenge to be studying for your clinical life and studying for anesthesiology exams during your intern year.

First priority: Complete Step 3

Don't blow this one off. You have to nail it the first time and be done with it. Take some time, study, do some questions, and schedule to get it knocked out. It might be helpful after doing a medicine or emergency medicine rotation. Study during these months, because you will be studying and practicing medicine for the exam.

I talked about this exam in chapter 14, but it is worth mentioning that this is a critical exam to complete and pass. We have resources for you at AnesthesiaMadeEasy.com/Step3.

Second priority: Prep for the ITE in February

This is the first time you will be taking the ITE. You might not have had any experience in the OR as a resident, but you will still be taking the exam. You don't want to completely stress about this one but you don't want to blow it off either.

You will be surprised how many of these questions you will be able to answer because: (1) you will have done anesthesia rotations while in medical school, and (2) there are a fair number of questions on the exam that are "straight medi-cine" that your intern year will help you prepare for. Your intern ITE is a great opportunity to see what the exam will be like and what to expect over the next few years.

AnesthesiaMadeEasy.com/ite is an excellent resource for your ITE preparation.

Third priority: Prep for the OR

You don't realize it, but you will be getting ready for the OR more than you know. You will be using your general knowl-edge as a physician to help guide you during your time in the OR. While this is true, you will also want to be studying anesthesia for your time in the OR.

I wrote an article at AnesthesiaMadeEasy.com/intern with some good ways you can prep for the USMLE, the ITE, and get ready for the OR with other resources and up to date tips. Instead of repeating the information here for filler, stop by the webpage and check it out.

26

Checklist for the Advanced Resident

CONGRATULATIONS ON YOUR decision to start your anesthesiology training. I know this was not an easy decision for you or one that you took lightly. Take heart. Your prior training will not be wasted. Your resident peers and your faculty will look to you to be a Subject Matter Expert (SME). A lot will be expected of you, especially if you are coming from another specialty. But I know you are up for it.

As an advanced resident, you will fall into one of three categories:

1. You are doing your CB year at another institution.

2. You are partway through your residency training in another specialty and you are "coming to the dark side" anesthesiology.

3. You have completed another residency and want to come back to train as an anesthesiologist.

First priority: Complete Step 3

You might have already completed USMLE/COMLEX Step 3 your intern year. If you have not, you need to make the Step 3 a priority. If you already have a license to practice medicine, you are even further along than your PGY-2 peers.

Completing your primary board certification for your first specialty

If you are completing another residency-training program before starting anesthesiology, you have the challenge of sitting for your primary board certification. This can be especially challenging when you are trying to study for anesthesiology at the same time. Much like studying for the USMLE/COMPLEX Step 3, the longer you wait, the more difficult it will become.

One option might be to study for and take the ITE and Basic exams, then go back and study for your Primary Certification early during your CA-2 year. How you want to manage this is up to you. You may decide to try and take your primary boards prior to the ITE/ Basic exams. This is a great question to discuss with your program director. You certainly do not want to fail the Basic exam. You want to pass it and move on with your training.

Prep for the OR

As an advanced resident, you may or may not have had any rotations in anesthesiology during your Intern year. Either way, doing a little reading to prepare for the OR is a good idea. I have an article on our website with some resources that will help you get OR ready for your CA-1 year at: AnesthesiaMadeEasy.com/or-ready

27

Checklist for Your CA-1 Year

ONE OF THE challenges of your CA-1 year is that it will feel like you are doing your Intern year all over again. There is such a huge learning curve. But, believe me, it is much better than your Intern year, because you are actually doing what you want to do—working as an anesthesiologist-in-training.

The ABA encourages residents to sign up for the ABA Portal as soon as you start your training. This allows them to directly communicate through a known e-mail to announce deadlines as they approach.

Finish Step 3
If you have not completed your Step 3, finish it off right now! You can't study effectively for the ITE and the Step 3.

In fact, put down this book right now, study for Step 3, and take the exam—then pick this book up again—I can wait.

Step 3 done?

Good. Let's get on with it.

Start preparing for the oral boards

Read chapters 9 thorough 17 and start putting the Applied exam techniques to work at the start of your CA-1 year. Ask your faculty to ask you questions as though they were during an oral board and give you feedback on your answers. It will help you sound smarter and it will help you practice for the exam.

You will be studying for the ITE and Basic exam by reading and doing questions. Additionally, answering your faculty's questions like the SOE will reinforce your knowledge by talking through the reasoning behind your anesthetic choices. The more practice you get doing this, the easier it will become.

If you start this early, it will make taking the Applied exam much easier.

Prep for the ITE—February is coming

Your first anesthesia exam as a CA-1 will be the Anesthesiology ITE in February. This ITE that you are taking will be **just four months before the Basic Exam**, so the stakes are high for you to study for both the ITE and starting prep for the Basic exam.

You will want to review two resources:

1. Review the content outline for the Basic Exam.
2. Review the specific Keywords that you missed on your last ITE.

If you did not take the exam before your CA-1 year, then you will need to focus on basic content outline to guide your study.

Since this is your last full-length "practice exam" before the Basic exam, you need to make the most out of it.

The ABA also has a list of areas that gave exam takers the most trouble.

Head to AnesthesiaMadeEasy.com/ITE to look up the content outline for the ITE to help you get ready. We also have a number of resources there to help you get ready for the exam.

Sign up for the Basic Exam

You will be signing up for the Basic Exam during your CA-1 year, which you will take at the end of your CA-1 year. You will want to sign up for the Basic Exam during the "Standard Registration" period (March–end of April) because it will save you about five hundred dollars if you don't have to sign up during the "Late Registration" period. (end of April to mid-May)

Put the deadline on your calendar and sign up early. Having an account at the ABA Portal will also help you not miss the deadlines.

Basic Exam will happen in June
It is GO TIME.

After you take the ITE, take a couple of weeks off from studying, then start your baseline studying. Keep a study schedule while you wait for the results from the ITE, usually in about six weeks. Review the ITE Keywords where you had problems. Also, take time to review the Keywords that were missed by most other residents as well.

These two sets of keywords should help you focus your preparation for the Basic Exam.

Focus on the ITE keywords that are related to Basic Exam Topics, because you have a little over three months to correct any glaring issues to do well on the Basic Exam.

If you scored really well on the ITE, don't slack off for the Basic exam. I know residents who crushed the ITE their CA-3 year, slacked off, and failed Part One of the Boards.[14] We have resources on our website AnesthesiaMadeEasy.com/ABA including links to the basic content outline, review books, and other resources to help you prepare for the first part of the board certification process.

---

14 This was when we only had the written exam (given after graduation) and the oral exam (given thereafter). The concept remains the same for you. You don't want to do well on the ITE in February only to fail Basic Exam in June.

28

Checklist for Your CA-2 Year

If you didn't pass the Basic Exam

THIS IS NOT the end of your career. If you did not pass the Basic exam, then you have a couple more chances to pass the exam so that you can progress in your training and graduate from residency. Individual programs set their own limits as to how many times you are allowed to fail the exam before you are dismissed form the program.

Don't mess around with this one. If you did not pass it your CA-1 year, then you need to reevaluate your studying and preparation for the Basic exam. This is not the time to make excuses; this is the time to be honest with yourself and dig into what really happened with the exam.

If you failed it, take some time to meet with your program director and get an academic coach. Find someone who can review your study schedule and preparation resources and help you come up with a better strategy. You have to pass this exam to advance in your training. Every time you have to retake the Basic Exam is more time and money focused on the Basic Exam and not the Advanced Exam (and it will add stress to your life).

Continue Applied Exam preparation

Continue to answer questions from your faculty like you are answering board examiners. Take every opportunity to do practice Applied exams through your residency.[15] When you take practice exams, focus on the skills you learned in chapter 23. Dissect the stem. Anticipate complications. Don't repeat the question. Practicing those skills is less about anesthesia knowledge and more about test taking technique. You will continue to add to your anesthesia knowledge as you study for the ITE.

Take your exams with your most intimidating faculty to help you get ready.

Accelerate Your ITE and Advanced Exam preparation

If you passed the Basic exam, then this is your green light to start focusing on the Advanced Exam while continuing to

---

15 Most of your faculty went through the old ABA system when they called it the oral board exam, therefore programs call these "mock orals."

review the things you missed on the Basic Exam. Use your ITE Keywords from last year to channel your studying for the ITE, which will happen again in February. During your CA-2 year, the ITE is the most important exam that you will be taking all year.[16] (Assuming you passed the Basic Exam.)

During your CA-2 year, you will start to rotate through more subspecialty rotations such as pediatric anesthesia, OB anesthesia, cardiac anesthesia, pain, and ICU. These rotations will help prepare you for the Advanced exam.

While you are on these rotations, read about these subspecialties and answer practice exam questions related to the subspecialty. Unlike medical school, where you were given shelf exams at the end of most rotations to gauge your mastery of the rotation, there are no formal exams, so you should build your own.

Review your keywords from the ITE you took during your CA-1 year and prepare for this next round of testing.

In the past, examinees relied heavily on old ACE exams. There have been some changes in the Advanced Exam, so the ACE questions might not be the only questions you should do.

When it comes to exam questions, do not rely only on test questions. They are helpful, but they should not be your only source of study materials.

-----

16 It also happens to be the only structured exam you will take all year.

29

Checklist for Your CA-3 Year

ONE MORE YEAR to go—unless you are doing a fellowship. With at least two ITEs under your belt and the Basic exam passed, it is easy to get complacent about your studying for the boards. The challenging cases that would keep you up the night before now don't even get your heart rate up.

"Oh. I've got a case tomorrow where my faculty wants an awake A-line, a triple lumen central line and an introducer for a Swan. Meh."

You are trying to see who has the fastest placement of a labor epidural in the department.

You have mastered the basics, now you want to improve your speed, time your anesthetic better, and have those crisp neuro wake ups.

When it comes to studying for Board Certification, you will need to fight "senioritis." It is easy to fall into the trap of thinking that you have the "anesthesiology thing" figured out. You are looking for a job or looking forward to your secured fellowship in your subspecialty—either way, you are not thinking about your board certification.

You have to get your head in the game.

Do not rely solely on how well you did on the ITE. You will have to continue to study to do well on the Advanced exams.

Figure out when you are going to get your medical license.

As part of the requirements to become board certified, you have to have an unexpired medical license by November fifteenth of the year that you take the Applied exam to get your results. It can be from any state, so as you tend to get closer to graduation, you need to consider obtaining this, even if you are planning on going on for fellowship.[17] You will not be able to complete your entire fellowship on a PIT. You will have to get a full medical license to meet this requirement.

Sign up for the Advanced Exam

Much like your CA-1 year, you will need to sign up for the Advanced exam. Again, make sure you register early in the

17 Texas tends to be a state that takes a while to get a medical license. (It can take up to nine months even if you have a clean record.) I know some residents who had to get a medical license in a state that was quicker to get, so they didn't miss the deadline. Start the process early.

March–May timeframe to save yourself some money on your road to board certification. Your ABA Portal communications will help you be aware of deadlines as they approach, buy you much be actively engaged.

ITE February

This is your last chance to take a full-length exam before the real thing. You have to ramp up your studying so that you can finish strong. By this point in your training, you should have a good handle on how you study best. Review your old keywords, go over the content outline for the ITE and see the areas that you are weak in.

Start going back through your old question books and old ACE exams to further your study.

This is a great opportunity to prepare for the Advanced exam.

Preparing for the Advanced Exam

By the time you get your scores back from the ITE, you should have a good idea what you are going to be doing after graduation from residency. You will know if you are starting work, going into fellowship, and how much time off you will have between the end of your residency and your next adventure.

You have to plan how you will spend your time as you finish up residency. If you know that you will have to start work or fellowship immediately after graduating, then you need to use the rest of your time in residency to study for the exam.

Senioritis is going to be difficult to fight against, but if your time is going to be limited after graduation, then you need to make the most of it.

If you are a chief resident, not only will you be doing the work of a CA-3, you will also have other responsibilities related to your administrative tasks. I wrote a short article at AnesthesiaMadeEasy.com/chief-resident to give you some guidance on how to continue to study for board certification while you are performing your demanding clinical and administrative duties.

Final Thoughts

The days are long, but the years are short.

—US Navy SEALs' saying

IF YOU ARE still reading this book, then, yes, you have a little OCD...you will fit into anesthesiology just fine.

One of the reasons I wrote this book was to help you successfully navigate the process of board certification in anesthesiology. After four years of medical school, plus a residency or two, you have finally arrived!

As overwhelming as the process of board certification can be, if you (1) break it down into manageable parts, and (2) spread your preparation throughout your training, board certification in anesthesiology is achievable.

Enjoy your training.

There will be no other time in your career that you will be in a dedicated environment to learn/study/practice anesthesiology.

As you go through your residency training, remember that board certification is not just about learning anesthesiology, it's about becoming a better anesthesiologist so that you can take care of patients.

Along the way, you will find people who help you by providing practice oral exams. They do it because they were once in your shoes. Once you are board certified, continue to "pay it forward" and help others.

As serious as the process of training is, it does not mean that you cannot have fun.

Don't forget to have fun.

Oh, and play the Game of Board Certification—and play it well.

Game On.

Thanks for reading *Anesthesiology Boards Made Easy*.

I have few things to ask of you.

1) If you would like to truly give me a toast, please take a moment and rate this book on Amazon.com; it is the single best thing you can do to thank me unless you hated the book. Then for the love of anesthesiology say nothing! Just kidding. If it is really that bad, then send me an e-mail and let me know how it could have been better.

2) Stop by AnesthesiaMadeEasy.com and see what else we have to offer. I am putting up new articles regularly that you should find helpful. All of the resources found in this book can be found on the website so that you easily find them on the web. I get a small finder's fee if you buy some of the resources through the links on the website, and it does not cost you anything. This helps me keep the website up and running and gives you a quick place to reference. It is a win-win for both of us.

3) Let others know about the book if you enjoyed it. Word of mouth is one of the best ways to let people know about this resource. (I wish I had it during my training.) Send your fellow residents over to AnesthesiaMadeEasy.com, and I am sure they will appreciate it.

4) Want to get in touch with me? Go to www. AnesthesiaMadeEasy.com and send me an e-mail.

Cheers:
Steiny

Made in the USA
Columbia, SC
05 February 2018